Ex LIBRARY BOOK
PAID FOR APRIL 1989

88

1988

9

Holmes
28·7·80

Design of
Racing Sports Cars

Colin Campbell

DESIGN OF
RACING SPORTS CARS

LONDON

CHAPMAN AND HALL

First published 1973
by Chapman and Hall Ltd
11 New Fetter Lane, London EC4P 4EE

© *1973 Colin Campbell*

Typeset by Preface Ltd, Salisbury,
and printed in Great Britain by
Whitstable Litho, Straker Brothers Ltd

S B N 412 11880 7

All rights reserved. No part of this book
may be reprinted, or reproduced or utilized in
any form or by any electronic, mechanical or
other means, now known or hereafter invented,
including photocopying and recording, or in
any information storage and retrieval system,
without permission in writing from the
Publisher.

CUMBERNAULD & KILSYTH
DISTRICT LIBRARY

ACC. NO.
094061

CLASS NO.
629.231

VENDOR | DATE
Holmes | 28.7.80

Contents

Contents

Preface

The engineering aspects of the design and construction of racing sports cars are our concern in this book. In it we analyse the functional behaviour of experimental or prototype sports cars as defined under Group 5 in Appendix 'J' of the International Sporting Code of the F.I.A. for 1973.

Since the F.I.A. committee responsible for defining such groups of racing cars has been all at sixes and sevens (one could even say at fives, sixes and sevens) over the last few years, it has been necessary to consider also the groups as they existed in 1970 and 1971 when Group 5 covered racing sports cars made in very limited production (25 or more per annum) and Group 6 covered experimental 'one-off' or prototype sports cars. The specialized class of two-seater racing car designed to compete under the rules· for the Canadian-American Challenge Cup, defined under Group 7 of Appendix 'J', is not considered in detail in this book, but apart from the restriction on engine capacity which applies to Group 5 cars competing in the World Championship for Makes, there is much in common in the basic design requirements of the two groups and the majority of the information in this book will be of interest to American and Canadian enthusiasts.

This is not a design textbook and the use of mathematics, where it cannot be avoided entirely, has been kept at a simple level. One need not be an architect to appreciate the utility and beauty of the flying buttresses of Notre Dame and a degree in engineering is not essential to appreciate the design subtleties of the modern racing sports car.

For more than two decades it has been only too clear in motor racing circles that the old concept of a sports car as a general purpose vehicle to be used for commuting to the office, for carrying home the groceries and for racing at the week-end is no longer valid. The author remembers watching about twenty years ago the visible evidence of rising blood

pressure on the faces of older members of the BARC, York-
shire Centre, as they watched the unloading of a very highly
modified BMW Type 328 sports car which arrived at meetings
in a van. Today it is not customary for such ordinary vehicles
as Group 2 (Special Touring Cars) to be driven to a race
meeting. It is no longer possible to compromise on this score
if one hopes to have a remote chance of winning. The Group
5 racing sports car is now a highly specialized vehicle,
expensive to design and manufacture, and its survival depends
upon the publicity value that is accorded by the discerning
public to the manufacturers of the cars that are successful.

From time to time certain manufacturers achieve notable
success in this field of motor sport endeavour, then retire for
several years, protesting at the expense. Such has been the
case with Jaguar, with Mercedes-Benz and now, after three
very successful years, with Porsche. A period of three or four
guaranteed years of stability in the rules governing this form
of motor sport would indeed be welcome to the majority of
small-production sports car manufacturers, such as Ferrari
and Porsche, Lola and Chevron. This would go a long way
towards reducing the financial burden of advertising their
wares by racing. Let there be no misunderstanding; the whole
automobile industry gains by the technical spin-off from
. motor racing.

Several books have been written on the racing history of
this class of vehicle. The author particularly recommends as
an introduction to the historical background 'The Racing
Sports Car' by Anthony Pritchard. It is assumed that the
reader is sufficiently acquainted with the rudiments of the
motor car, with the working of the four-cycle engine, the
gearbox, the suspension system, etc., in a general way. The
more specialized design features of the modern racing sports
car will be described to the best of the author's ability. This
is not false modesty: in these days of specialization and
increasing design sophistication it would be difficult to find
any author who could claim to be an expert on every aspect
of the sports car.

The author is particularly indebted to the Institution of
Mechanical Engineers for granting permission to use material
from Dr Hans Mezger's excellent paper 'The Development of

the Porsche Type 917 Car.' The Ford Motor Company have also been most helpful in supplying information on the design, testing and development of the whole range of GT40 sports cars.

Colin Campbell

Nunthorpe, Cleveland County
February 1973

CHAPTER ONE
Evolution

IMPROVING THE BREED

One cannot fail to notice the lamentations in the motoring press at the fate of several Formula 1 constructors who are now said to be drifting, as the price of sponsorship, into a gradual acceptance of their own anonymity. Some day perhaps the motor racing public will be saying 'but surely John Player and Marlboro employ people to make these cars, don't they!'

Something of the original competitive spirit that animated the automobile industry at the turn of the century still remains nevertheless in sports car racing. Let us admit the teams accept sponsorship, but in the main the sponsors are selling products that *could* be used by the competing cars, such products as petrol and tyres and sparking plugs and lubricating oil. We have it on good authority that they actually use the same oil as we put in our own engines, although the tyres don't exactly look like the ones on our Volkswagen.

That astute aspiring Henry Ford really hated Motor Racing, but he forced himself in 1901 to face up to the terrors of blow-outs and spin-outs on the frozen surface of Lake St Claire to gain publicity for the automobiles he was trying to sell to the public. His grandson, Henry Ford II, a little more fascinated by the sport and no less astute was prepared to spend millions of dollars to make a Ford sports car with only one object in mind – to win at Le Mans. Even though the products he sells by the million bear no outward resemblance to the GT40s that won at Le Mans there remains, long after this sales promotional exercise, a large bank of knowledge and experience stored away in the files and computers of the Ford Motor Company that helps them to improve the handling and general behaviour of the cars they sell to us.

1

In case the reader suspects that Ford have supplied the writer with a Capri GT3000 'on permanent loan' let us turn to that 'sea green incorruptible' *Motor Sport* a magazine that lost the financial support of advertising from a large British car maker for several years for their outspoken comments on two post-war mediocre models made by that particular company. This is what they say about a new model recently introduced by Ford of Britain: 'The Granada is a larger step forward than usually occurs when a manufacturer brings out a new model and I would say that a lot of Ford's racing know-how has gone into the new Granada, to make their business-man's express a that much better road car'. Our quotation from *Motor Sport* of July 1972 is given simply to show that after all these years the hardened professional scribes still have a little faith in that hoary old saying 'Motor Racing improves the Breed'.

The direct financial rewards of sports car racing have never been high and the late W.O. Bentley would have been the first to admit this, yet the gains in publicity and in design know-how made by the racing Bentleys should not be underestimated. It was the Wall Street Crash, followed by the Depression that dried up the demand for such luxuries as craftsman-built motor cars, that put the old Bentley firm out of business. In a more stable economy the Bentley Company must surely have survived and prospered. The E Type Jaguar is a better car than it would ever have been if Jaguar had never raced and who would ever dispute that the Porsche in its production form has not been enhanced immeasurably by racing development.

THE TRADITIONAL AUTOMOBILE

Early racing cars automatically followed the pattern of the established passenger car. Little imagination was needed to see that the removal of as much of the body as possible and the provision of a larger capacity engine would give a car more acceleration and increase the maximum speed. By the turn of the century the more advanced manufacturers were establishing a pattern that was to survive in its essential chassis layout to the present day. As a successful layout for a racing car or a sports car it was to survive for half a century.

Let us then describe the 1901 Mercedes, for this is the car that is chosen by the majority of motoring historians, as the great grandfather of the car we ride in today. Gottleib Daimler had been dead for a year when Wilhelm Maybach produced a new Daimler model, the first of the new line to be called 'Mercedes' at the request of the influential industrialist Emile Jellinek. The name 'Daimler' was too German-sounding for the car to sell well in France, so Jellinek's daughter Mercedes gave her name to a line of wonderful cars that looks like surviving as long as the motor car itself.

Not all the components on the 1901 Mercedes have survived unchanged, but the basic layout remains. We no longer use chain drive to the rear wheels or magneto ignition. The front wheels (and sometimes the rear) are independently sprung and we now find it necessary to fit brakes to the front wheels as well as the back. The engine on Maybach's car was at the front, with cooling radiator placed ahead of the engine. Two components were used to give the required speed reduction between the engine and the road wheels. The gearbox, although crude in design, was placed behind the engine and was unchanged in principle from the manual gearbox in use today. The final drive was by chain and sprocket, with the larger sprocket fitted to one driven rear wheel to give a second speed reduction.

THE FRONT–ENGINED RACING TRADITION

Daimler-Benz A.G. seem to be unique in the length of their racing tradition. It has not been a continuous involvement with motor sport and some cynics would say this lack of continuity could well be the reason for their survival since motor racing is so expensive. The Mercedes racing tradition survived the amalgamation with the more sober-minded Benz management in 1926 and it is even possible they benefited technically from the cross-fertilization of ideas; there was certainly no lack of ingenuity shown when they decided to return for a third bout of competitive development in 1952.

Let us then use the changes that occurred with each re-entry of this old company into the arena of motor sport to

illustrate the persistence of one successful chassis layout,
namely the tradition of putting the engine at the front, while
continuing to drive the rear wheels.

The 1927–31 Mercedes S Series

The family resemblance between the 1914 GP Mercedes
(which was really a two-seater sports car with the mudguards
removed) and the 1929 SSK Mercedes sports car is quite
uncanny. Even the wedge-shaped radiator with its famous
three-pointed star emblem had hardly changed. The straight-
sided channel-section chassis frame, upswept over the front
and rear semi-elliptic springs was perhaps a little deeper in
section. The two spare wheels were still mounted at an angle
behind the body and the body sides were still cut away to
give the driver plenty of elbow room.

The SSK was about 30 m.p.h. faster than the 1914 GP car,
which is no great improvement after 15 years and with an
engine capacity of 7 litres and the use of a supercharger to
attain this maximum of about 120 m.p.h. one wonders why a
little more thought was not given to reducing the drag of the
stark body with its generous frontal area. The rate of
acceleration with the supercharger in use was at least twice
that of the 1914 GP Mercedes and was superior to that of the
4.5 litre 'Blower Bentley'. Unfortunately the large type
supercharger, 'the Elephant Blower', that gave a boost of 12
lb/in^2 and was used in competition from 1930 could not be
used for a longer period than twenty seconds if the life of the
engine was not to be in jeopardy.

The use of the supercharger to raise the induction pressure
above atmospheric pressure was no novelty and had been
used on an American Chadwick in 1908. Gottlieb Daimler
had patented the use of a compressor to increase the
induction pressure as early as 1885 and his son Paul had
experimented in the years following the first world war with
reciprocating compressors and eccentric-vane type compressors and had finally settled on the Roots blower, an
American invention, as the most reliable for use in the
post-war Mercedes. Paul Daimler left Daimler Motoren
Gesellshaft in 1922 and his replacement as Chief Engineer

was a young Austrian engineer, Dr Ferdinand Porsche, well-known for his successful designs of Austro-Daimler.

Despite the tremendous pressure put on him in these early years with the company Ferdinand Porsche devoted considerable time to the design and development of the S series of supercharged touring and sports cars. The 250 b.h.p. SSK was the last of the series designed under his supervision and the lightened and more powerful (reputedly 300 b.h.p.) version, the SSKL, in which Caracciola won the Mille Miglia in 1931 was designed after Hans Nibel had succeeded to the position of Chief Engineer in 1928. Dr Porsche returned to his native Austria as Chief Engineer of the little Steyr Company. He was suffering from overwork, having been responsible in a period of no more than six years for the design of 65 different types of vehicle, from passenger cars to military vehicles. Even Detroit for all its reputation, never drove its top people so hard.

All the S Series of Mercedes were fitted with 7-litre engines having six cylinders in-line and a single overhead camshaft to operate two valves per cylinder. The 1914 GP Mercedes four-cylinder engine had been based on an earlier aero-engine design. All four cylinders were machined from separate steel billets and with sheet steel water jackets welded around each cylinder and exposed valve springs above the cylinders the engine looked very antique by our present standards. Even so the Mercedes Company had developed this method of construction to give a very light and perfectly reliable engine and a change to the *en bloc,* principle using cast-iron for the cylinder block and crankcase would invariably result in a heavier engine. Porsche therefore decided to adopt the lightest available alloy, aluminium, not only for the cylinder block, but for the crankcase too. Moreover, and this was a very bold step at this time, he had the two components cast as a single unit. The cylinder head, however, he had cast in iron since the use of aluminium alloy with inserted valve seats of a different material had not been developed at that time. It was the differential expansion between the cast-iron head and the aluminium alloy block that was to lead to one of the few weaknesses in this new design of engine, a tendency to head gasket failure. The crankshaft was a fully-machined

forging with four large diameter main bearings and at the
front end it drove the Roots supercharger through a pair of
bevel wheels and a clutch. The blower was mounted vertically
in front of the cylinder block and the clutch was arranged to
be put out of engagement until the driver pressed the
accelerator pedal the final inch to the floor boards.

Following the custom of other quality engines of the
period there were two plugs per cylinder, one sparked by coil
ignition to give easy starting and a good spark at low engine
speeds, the other sparked by a magneto to give a good spark
at high speeds.

In the chassis the most obvious change was the disap-
pearance of the external chain drive to be replaced by the
customary enclosed rear axle bevel drive and torque tube
universally jointed immediately behind the gearbox. In other
respects, however it was not easy to observe any essential
changes from Maybach's 1914 design. The similitude is of
course deceptive. Much had been learned in the few years of
active racing since the end of the war in the subtleties of
making a semi-elliptically sprung racing car handle well and the
SSK (K for *kurz* or short, to indicate the short chassis model)
handled as well as any sports car of the period and certainly
better than the majority.

When Mercedes raced again it was with independent
suspension at both ends of the car and this revolutionized the
handling of sports and racing cars in one giant step, as big a
step forward as we have since seen repeated in the development of the low-profile tyre.

The 300SL and 300SLR Mercedes Sports Cars

The new Mercedes sports car that appeared in 1952 was built
with very little regard to cost or selling price. In its main
design features, however, it represents the major developments that had taken place in sports car design since the days
of the SSK. Rudi Uhlenhaut was now the Chief Engineer, no
newcomer to motor racing since he had worked on the
Mercedes GP cars in the years immediately preceding the war
and had been responsible for designing the special 1.5-litre
'Voiturette Class' car which won the Tripoli Grand Prix in
1939.

The old idea of a ladder-type channel section frame had now disappeared into limbo, to be replaced by a tubular space-frame to support the engine, transmission parts, passengers and body and to resist all the torsional loads and bending stresses fed into the structure by the attachments of the suspension systems at front and rear. A certain sacrifice in convenience was necessary in this particular design since the tubular frame in the region of the body sills was wide and deep, reducing the less agile to an undignified sliding scramble when getting into the car. To assist entry, however, there was the up-and-over gull-wing door and this in itself seems to have had such a fascination for the unpredictable public that the change to more normal doors and the reduction in sill-height that came with the re-designed '300SL Roadster', intended for the American market, was not received with any enthusiasm. From personal experience the author would gladly accept either model as a Christmas present. With or without gull-swing doors the 300SL was a delightful car to drive and had a special charm for anyone with a feel for fine engineering.

It soon proved after its introduction in 1952 that it could take on the finest sports cars in Europe, Aston Martin, Jaguar and Ferrari. They were beaten by Ferrari in the Mille Miglia, but they won at Le Mans and came in 1-2-3-4 on their home ground at the Nürburgring.

The suspension was of course independent all round, with unequal-length wishbones and coil springs at the front and swing-axles, in the Mercedes and Benz racing car tradition, at the rear. The high roll-centre and large camber changes associated with swing-axle suspension made the handling of the car less than perfect in the hands of the average driver and there was a tendency to excessive oversteer. The same has been said so many times of the early designs of Volkswagen, but the Volkswagen was never intended for racing.

By 1955 the 300SL was no longer competitive in international sports car racing, despite the introduction of a lightweight body and a change to direct fuel injection and its place was taken in the field of sports car racing by a new 300 SLR (R for racing) which was based on many components from the very successful 1954 Grand Prix car, the Type W196. The 300 SLR was designed expressly for racing and was never sold to the public. Only nine were made and it is estimated that they each cost £35 000 ($85 000) to build. The tubular frame on this machine was even more complex, yet much lighter than on the normal SL and the whole body, an open one this time since the drivers preferred it this way, was constructed in magnesium alloy. Many of the engine and transmission components were also made from magnesium alloy castings. The straight-8 engine was installed in the frame at an angle of 70° to the vertical to get a much lower body profile at the front and Bosch fuel injection direct into each combustion chamber and desmodromic (push-pull cam operation) valve gear were used, exactly as in the smaller GP engine.

To reduce the extent of the oversteer a modified form of swing-axle was devised with the pivot located below the final drive casing and the roll resistance at the rear increased by the addition of a horizontal compensating spring (see Fig 1.1).

A 300SLR in the Ford Museum at Dearborn, near Detroit, carries a notice to the effect that this car won every race in which it started. This is no doubt true for the particular car in the museum, but one at least failed to finish in most horrifying circumstances at Le Mans in 1955. It was Pierre Levegh's crash into the packed crowds at Le Mans that led to the withdrawal of Mercedes-Benz from all forms of motor

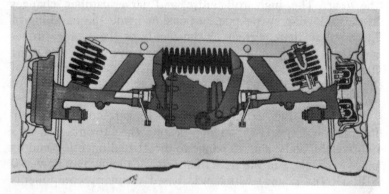

Fig 1.1   Rear Swing axle on the 300 SLR.g

racing. The dangerous location of the pits, which has since been changed, was undoubtedly a major contributory factor in the tragedy, but to our great regret we no longer see the famous three-pointed encircled star on the racing circuits of the world.

The Mercedes C111

At the Frankfurt Show in September 1969 there appeared before the public a new Mercedes Coupe, the C111, which was ostensibly a design exercise to test the Daimler-Benz rotary combustion engine made under licence from the original Wankel company. Perhaps it will never race, but it does represent the latest thinking in a long line of Mercedes sporting vehicles and as such deserves our attention.

At last we witness a final break with the tradition established by Maybach in 1901. For two-thirds of a century Daimler, followed by Daimler-Benz, have believed it is wrong to 'put the cart before the horse' and now in the C111 we see an admission that the engine can be placed in a location which we usually call 'mid-engine' and is really just ahead of the rear wheels.

In many respects the C111 makes an unconscious acknowledgement to the development work carried out by other more active racing car designers in the fourteen years since the Company abandoned motor racing. The body is in glass-fibre reinforced plastic and has a strong resemblance to many modern mid-engined sports cars such as the Lotus Europa and the de Tomaso Pantera, but the gull-wing doors are a nostalgic reminder of the 300SL. Rear suspension is now unequal-length wishbones, being very close to contemporary racing practice with short upper transverse links, long lower ones and double radius arms for fore and aft location of the wheel hub carriers. Very little now remains of the old Daimler-Benz traditions, unless of course we mention in passing the unsurpassed engineering skills in design and execution.

NATURAL SELECTION

The workings of human creativity in any field of endeavour bear a strong reminder of Darwin's Theory of Natural Selection. A new idea is born, almost like a biological mutation, and if the new concept proves to be more successful in the particular environment than the older ideas it survives. With the passage of time the old ideas die out, like the dodo and the mammoth. A good example in automobile engineering was the use of an open propeller shaft and two universal joints to drive the rear axle. Nobody believed that the chain drive could survive for long, but for many years the Hotchkiss drive fought for survival against the alternative design in which the propeller shaft was enclosed by a torque tube which moved up and down with the rear axle casing at the outer end and was universally mounted at the gearbox end. This system was favoured by many clever engineers since it relieved the semi-elliptic rear springs from all torque wind-up when accelerating and braking. The Hotchkiss design, however, after years of development proved the more acceptable for general passenger car use and the torque tube disappeared.

To design a car with only rear wheel brakes may seem ridiculous to us now, but the introduction of front wheel brakes caused many heads to shake: tyre wear would be excessive and if the front wheels were ever to lock when braking the driver would be helpless since he could no longer steer the car. The 1914 French Grand Prix was won by one of the very fast Mercedes cars which was discussed earlier and these only had rear wheel brakes. Writing in 'The Autocar' however of the much slower Peugeots which were fitted with four wheel brakes, H. Massac Buist said: 'time and again the Peugeots would escape being overhauled by the occurrence of corners, on approaching which they enjoyed the immense advantage over Mercedes and Sunbeam who were obviously quicker to accelerate and fleeter when at full speed. Front wheel brakes must have been worth anything up to a minute a lap to the Peugeots'.

How obvious so many of these evolutionary steps appear to us today as we look back across half a century of development. Four wheel brakes, hydraulic brake operation, independent suspension, short-stroke engines, twin overhead camshafts using piston-type tappets, streamlined bodies, disc brakes, wide-section tyres (so obvious we could kick ourselves!) and so many other changes that we now take for granted. One conflict is still not yet resolved, despite the improved grip on the road given by modern tyres and the exploitation of aerofoils, and that is the application of four wheel drive to racing cars. Later, in Chapters Four, Five and Six, we will consider all three transmission modes, including front wheel drive, and examine the influence each form of transmission has on the behaviour of a racing sports car when accelerating, cornering and braking.

In this whole evolutionary process of sports and racing car development there remain two controversial aspects of design that deserve our attention in this initial examination of the design problems that confront the automobile engineer. The first is the question of front wheel drive, so successful in modern rallies, yet so much a memory in motor racing. The second is the chequered history of the rear-engined or mid-engined racing car, which many said was almost impossible to drive in the pre-war days of the P-Wagen, yet is seen today as the only way to succeed and is reasonably safe in the hands of dozens of young men who could never have survived against such giants as Nuvolari and Rosemeyer.

Since the historical impact came first we will take a look first at that fascinating vehicle, the front wheel drive racing car and for the rest of the book we will use the following abbreviations: for front wheel drive, FWD; for rear wheel drive, RWD and for four wheel drive 4WD.

FRONT WHEEL DRIVE

FWD cars were on the scene quite early. There was an FWD Dutch Spyker in 1902 and in 1905 an American Christie was raced with an enormously heavy beam front axle suspended on semi-elliptic springs with the drive taken to the front wheels. Twenty years elapsed before Jimmy Murphy, the Indianapolis driver, persuaded Harry Miller to design an FWD car to be raced on the board tracks of the period. This was in 1924 and the design was very successful.

In Great Britain the first production sports car with FWD was the 1.5-litre four cylinder Alvis designed by Capt G Smith Clarke. Two unblown cars competed unsuccessfully at Le Mans and a blown version developing 75 b.h.p. finished

second in the 1928 TT. In 1929 Alvis made a 1.5-litre
straight-8 racing sports car with a supercharged output of 125
b.h.p. It competed with both single and two-seater bodywork
and won its class in the 1929 Tourist Trophy race.

The Czech firm of Tracta also made an FWD sports car
about the same period, a car that was renowned for its ability
to corner fast in European speed hill climbs.

The classic L–29 Cord of 1930-32 and the latter versions,
the Model 810 and 812, often called 'the coffin-nosed Cords',
were designed by a brilliant young engineer who had worked
for Duesenberg. More than 2000 of Gordon Buehrig's more
familiar coffin-nosed design were made and the few that
remain have become collector's items in America.

FWD in Action

The success of the FWD Miller in American racing is not in
dispute, yet today in America only Oldsmobile make a car
with FWD and apart from a few experiments with 4WD the
racing and sports cars are all driven at the rear. The writer
became aware of the problems associated with FWD when he
made his first journey by FWD in 1942 from Farnborough to
Lancashire on a surface of hard-packed snow in a BSA Scout
sports car with almost bald tyres (new ones being unobtain-
able at the time). He recalled the oft-repeated maxim 'FWD is
most stable when accelerating through a corner' and he found
this to be perfectly correct if only one was clever enough to
judge the approach speed so that one could actually
accelerate through the bend. If however one approached the
corner at a speed that was only two or three miles per hour in
excess of the safe cornering speed, i.e. safe for the acceleration technique, there appeared to be no way of getting round
the corner safely. Lifting the foot from the throttle only
reduced cornering power and the car went into a spin. If
however one was brave enough to keep the pedal in the same
position on the accelerator the car ran wide, often finishing
on the wrong side of the road. Rally drivers in FWD
Mini-Coopers have developed ways of 'scrubbing off' speed
when they realise they are approaching a bend at too high a
speed and this is certainly a triumph for human ingenuity,
but the secret of driving a Miller FWD race car on a known

circuit was to find the safe speed round every bend and never, repeat never, exceed that speed. A study of the dynamics of cornering with FWD is given in Chapter Five.

The Mechanics of FWD

The FWD cars that were made forty years ago and earlier all suffered mechanically from the same crying need. Nobody had yet devised a sound reliable *constant velocity* universal joint. The only U/Js available at the time of the Miller and the Alvis were variants on the well-known Hooke's joint (see Fig. 1.2). The simple Hooke's joint only gives a constant velocity drive, through the whole 360° of one revolution, when the shaft it is driving is exactly in line with the driving shaft. When the driven shaft is at angle to the driving shaft the speed fluctuates during every 90° of rotation. With an angular displacement of 8° between the two shafts the variation in speed of the driven shaft is only ±2 per cent, but with a relative angle of 30° the variation becomes as high as 15 per cent. The variation can be cancelled out by means of two Hooke's joints at right angles, which is the method used on the passenger car propeller shaft, but even here the three shafts must stay in the same vertical plane if no torque or velocity variation is to occur. The early FWD cars did not meet these requirements and the cyclical torque variations, particularly at large steering angles, put a high strain on the universal joints and often caused them to wear out far too rapidly. The early designs of Cord suffered in this way, the Alvis flexible joints were unreliable and, from personal experience, the writer can say that the inner flexible joints on the B.S.A. Scout only lasted about 10 000 miles.

It is of course quite possible that Necessity is the Mother of Invention. Unfortunately the period of gestation is sometimes painfully long. The Rzeppa joint was the invention that these early FWD designers so badly needed. but it was only patented by A.H. Rzeppa in 1926 and not marketed until the middle of the Thirties. Gordon Buehrig was able to use it on his Model 810 Cord which appeared in 1936. Effectively the Rzeppa joint was a ball and socket joint in which both ball and socket were grooved to accommodate hardened steel balls. As shown in Fig 1.3, which is a Birfield

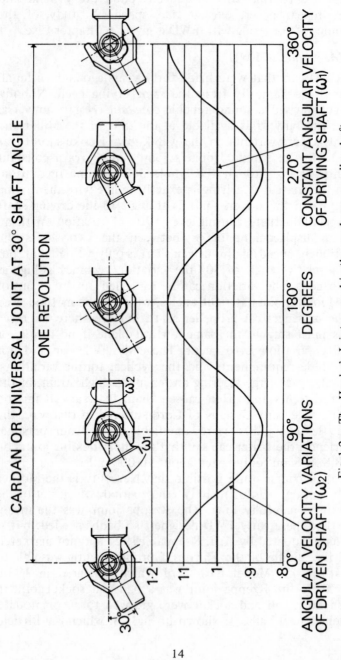

Fig 1.2 The Hooke's Joint as used in the modern propeller shaft.

14

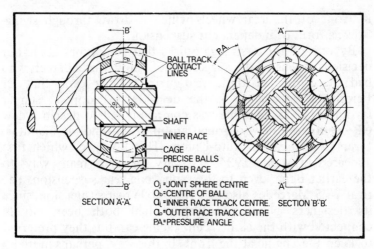

Fig 1.3   The Birfield-Rzeppa Joint.

Joint, a modern version of the Rzeppa, a ball cage is used to guide the six balls and hold them in what is called the *median plane*, this being a plane which passes through the point of intersection of the centre-lines of the two shafts at all times.

This Birfield Joint, made by Hardy-Spicer, was the means whereby Alec Issigonis could provide reliable FWD to the famous Mini and the fantastically successful Mini Cooper S.

THE REAR–ENGINED REVOLUTION

This phrase, so popular with motoring journalists, refers to the change in engine location from front to rear that started on sports and racing cars in the Fifties and has culminated in the last decade in the only acceptable position for an engine in a racing car being immediately in front of the rear wheels. Many of these journalists have too short memories or too little interest in events that occurred before they were born. If this was a revolution what happened to the earlier coups? For example there was a Grand Prix Benz that raced unsuccessfully for two seasons, in 1923 and 1924. It is best remembered for its remarkable 'tear-drop' body designed by Dr Rumpler, but it did also have other interesting features. The engine was located towards the rear; in fact immediately in front of the rear wheels which it drove through swing-axles, a form of independent suspension.

By one of those strange quirks that sometimes guide our decisions it was at the suggestion of Adolf Rosenberger, who had raced one of these rear-engined Benz cars, that Dr Ferdinand Porsche took the decision to adopt a similar layout in 1933 when he was commissioned to design a new GP car for the newly-formed group of automobile manufacturers to be called Auto-Union. This P-Wagen, which first appeared in March 1934, was very similar in many ways to the earlier Benz, even to the swing-axle rear suspension. The rival W25 Mercedes also had swing-axle rear suspension, since its designers Nibel and Wagner had both been closely connected with the earlier Benz racing car, but they preferred to keep the engine at the front. In this way, perhaps more by good fortune than by intention, they avoided the inherent perils of the P-Wagen design, to wit a rearward weight-bias, swing axle rear suspension, and to complete the terrible trio, *a driver seated well forward of the centre of gravity.*

The late Laurence Pomeroy in Volume 1 of 'The Grand Prix Car', described the failings of the Auto-Union as follows: 'With nearly 60 per cent of the weight carried on the rear wheels, and the exceptionally high roll-centre at the rear brought about by the use of the swing-axle system, the cars were fundamentally inclined to oversteer, and owing to the extremely forward mounting of the driver the tail could move through a considerable angle before the pilot realized the break-away point had been reached'.

The driver was placed fairly close to the ground and was deep inside the high body sides. His feet were a few inches behind the front wheel centre line and between him and the rear engine was a wedge-shaped fuel tank. The engine was ahead of the rear axle in what is now regarded as the orthodox position for a Grand Prix car and the gearbox was behind the final drive. The engine in this first Auto-Union, designed for the 750 kg Formula, was a V–12 of 4.36 litres and was obviously longer than the current 3–litre engines. This fact plus the additional ten inches or so required for the wedge fuel tank placed the driver well forward of the C.G. The fuel tank was placed close to the C.G. to prevent any appreciable change in the handling characteristics from full to empty tanks. This is still recognized as a most desirable aim, as of course was the attempt to place the main masses close to the C.G. to make the car more responsive to quick changes in direction.

Despite these criticisms of the handling of the P-Wagen the car was still successful, particularly since Mercedes were not free from teething troubles with their new model. One obvious advantage of the Auto-Union design was the much lower frontal area that could be achieved with no propeller shaft in the way. Hans Stuck was one of the few drivers able to cope with the problems of handling this car and in that first year of competition he became the Champion Driver of Germany.

During the development of the P-Wagen from A Type to C Type there was a stage by stage increase in engine capacity, blower capacity and, naturally, in power output. The C Type developed 520 b.h.p. against the original 295 b.h.p. of the A Type and despite the modifications made to the rear suspension and the gradually repositioning of the driver closer to the C.G. the tremendous torque that was now available made the problem of oversteer on corners even more acute. After a poor season in 1935 the following year was a successful one for Auto-Union despite the opposition from a new Mercedes, with a shorter wheelbase, a more streamlined body and a re-designed rear swing-axle suspension. The Mercedes however also proved something of a handful in this new form and was also handicapped by unreliability.

Mercedes, unhappy with swing-axle suspension, were working on another completely new layout in 1936, and from the design team of Wagner, Hess and Uhlenhaut there appeared a new car in 1937, designated the W125, which used a sophisticated version of the old De Dion suspension at the rear, double wishbones and coil springs at the front and hydraulic shock absorbers instead of the unpredictable friction type previously so popular for racing cars. The Mercedes now had a new engine with an output of 640 b.h.p. against the 520 b.h.p. of the Auto-Union and the improved handling and higher power of the Mercedes made it almost invincible. Auto-Union did have some success during this last year of the 750 kg Formula and the remarkable ability of such drivers as Nuvolari, Rosemeyer and Stuck to control these tail-sliding monsters was demonstrated repeatedly.

Even so, when Dr Porsche left the Auto-Union racing organization in 1937 to start work on the Volkswagen, the new design team decided immediately to follow the example of Mercedes and abandon the swing-axle. This new D Type Auto-Union was the work of Feuereissen, von Eberhorst and Werner. The De Dion rear suspension they devised was much simpler than that on the Mercedes. A Panhard rod was used for transverse location and forward-running radius arms on both sides for longitudinal location. With suitable modification of the double wishbone suspension at the front the car was now basically understeering in most corners, and only a moderate amount of oversteer could be provoked by using full traction in a corner. Other changes were made to make the car a little easier to drive. The fuel tanks were placed on each side of the driver, as in the modern GP cars, and the driver was now sitting very close to the C.G.

One cannot oversimplify the analysis of the development of the Auto-Union in the above manner without the danger of implying that the handling problems of this rear-engined car were solved as soon as Dr Porsche left. Given time, far less time than the vast majority of automobile engineers of his day, Dr Porsche would undoubtedly have sorted out the handling of the Auto-Union. It would be presumptuous of a technical journalist to try to guess what solutions he would have adopted. What matters is that we know that the problems were solved and that it was only the intervention of the war that made us forget all about rear-engined cars when racing re-commenced in 1947—or was it the engineering ability of Daimler-Benz that had clouded the issue?

The Post-War Revolution

Business Training Schools run very popular courses today and we can certainly recommend the food. Those of us with time on our hands to attend such courses are told such platitudes as 'identify your successes and failures; then build on your successes'. The Cooper Car Company were so successful immediately after the war making rear-engined Formula 3 racing cars with 500c.c. motor-cycle engines that they must have no time to spare to attend such valuable courses. How else can we explain why John Cooper made his first sports car in 1949 with a conventional front-engine, rear-drive layout? One reason could be that he wished to use readily available relatively cheap components, at first from Vauxhall motors and later from MG. Even so, it was not until 1955 that the Cooper-Climax sports car appeared with an 1100 c.c.| single OHC engine fitted at the rear. Nine years had passed by this time since the early successes of the Cooper 500s. Of course, this was still a low-powered car and it could still be argued at this time that rear-engines were all right for underpowered sports cars like the Porsche and the Cooper, but would be intrinsically unsound for big sports cars and Grand Prix cars.

Despite the successes of the Cooper-Climax in its class it was not until the early Sixties that the majority of racing sports car makers began to realise that a revolution had really happened. Ferrari for example refused to believe it and they were cautious enough to make cars of both types for several years. Colin Chapman had followed Cooper in the Grand Prix field with the 1960 Mark 18 Lotus, but it was not until 1962 that he followed up with a racing sports car with a rear engine, the Lotus Type 23.

The author makes no claims as a historian, not even in this specialized field, but it does appear to him that the rear-engined layout used by Dr Porsche in the P-wagen *never really died*. When Dr Porsche left Auto-Union in 1937 and was given a clean sheet of drawing paper and told to design a 'People's Car' he immediately designed a car with a rear engine and swing-axle rear suspension. Admittedly he had to forget the Volkswagen for several unforgettable years while he designed other more formidable vehicles like the 'Tiger', tank, but with this lapse of several years in continuity the line of succession from the C type Auto-Union passes via the humble VW to the first car to carry the name Porsche which was built in 1947 with a slightly tuned 1100c.c. VW power unit, a simple tubular chasis and an open two-seater body. Since Dr Porsche's son Ferry had no other components available at this time the first production Porsche, which came in 1949, used the normal VW drive system and suspension parts. The official entry of Porsche into sports car racing began in 1954, the year the Cooper-Climax appeared with its 'revolutionary rear-engine'. So began the conflict all over again, this time between Ferry Porsche and the swing-axle. The VW and the Porsche had both been reasonably well-behaved as low-powered passenger vehicles, with only an occasional tendency to rear-end misbehaviour in the wet, but the gradual increase in power to weight ratio and the higher cornering speeds used in racing soon re-introduced 'the swing-axle syndrome'. John Cooper had no such problem since he was using a type of unequal length double wishbone suspension at the back, in which the transverse leaf spring acted as one of the wishbones.

By 1957 with the latest racing sports Porsche, the RSK 1600, the dry weight had dropped to 1150 lb and the power had increased to 148 b.h.p. Oversteer was reduced by the use of a modified swing-axle system which used transverse radius arms pivoted below the gearbox casing to drop the level of the roll-centre.

Eventually the modified swing-axle was abandoned and the RSK fitted with a typical wishbone system. complete with fore and aft radius arms and coil springs. Other Porsche models appeared even later than the RSK in which various forms of semi-trailing link suspension were used at the rear, but the message was now received and understood. Tyre profiles were changing rapidly and there was now only one tested system of suspension that would keep the outer wheel close to zero camber in a corner and this is the system that Porsche have used since. The Type 917 was the latest of this line of rear-engined cars that trace their ancestry back to the P-wagen. Since the introduction of a 3-litre limit in 1972 to Prototype sports car racing Porsche have withdrawn from racing, but the Type 917 was such a landmark in racing sports car design that the author has devoted a special Appendix to a full description of this magnificent machine.

THE CONTEMPORARY SCENE

It would have been very enjoyable if we could have continued to use the same sports car for going to the movies, for collecting the groceries and for blasting round a race circuit at the week-end. Cars like the M.G. Midget, the Austin Healey, the Triumph TRs and the Jaguar XK120 were used in this way and one can still have fun with them in the smaller club events, if one is not too anxious to win. Commercial pressures exist, however, on the manufacturers of sports cars to persuade them to produce special prototype or experimental sports cars that will gain publicity by winning races. The XK120 was an excellent sports car, but to beat the much more expensive Ferraris the Jaguar Company had to make a racing version, the C Type, which was less of a road car and finally the D Type which *could* be driven to the races but only from sheer bravado. Aston Martin were forced to develop the DB3 into the DB3S and Mercedes-Benz who had a very roadworthy sports car in the 300SL were forced by the pressure of competition to develop a full-blooded *racing* sports car, the unbeatable 300SLR which used an enlarged version of the Formula 1 engine and most expensive alloys throughout the whole chassis and the body. The fact that the Chief Engineer, Rudi Uhlenhaut, used one frequently on the road is more a tribute to his skill and cool temperament than to the suitability of the 300SLR for use on the public highway.

Since humankind in general shows a remarkable aptitude for finding loopholes in the law the control of Motor Sport throughout the world is almost as complex in its many ramifications as the United Nations. Every year *La Federation Internationale de l'Automobile (*(the F.I.A.) holds a meeting of its *Commission Sportive Internationale* (the C.S.I.) to review the sporting regulations, the championship rules and any necessary amendments to the regulations that they deem to be necessary. If they have a failing it is a tendency to make too many changes in the championship rules. One can no longer design and develop a racing car or racing sports car for a new formula in a matter of months or for a few thousand pounds. The writer has no personal involvement on either side but he is conscious of the great loss we all suffered when Porsche, after their considerable expenditure in 1969 when they made twenty five of the Type 917 cars, with the new flat-12 4.5-litre engine, in order to compete in Group 5 (at that time the Sports Car Group) found their very successful car virtually outlawed by the changes in the rules within a period of two years. In 1972 the prototype or experimental Group was now called Group 5, Group 6 had disappeared and the 'small-scale production' Group 4 was in effect the Special GT car, of which 500 had to be manufactured. Moreover, as a final discouragement, the Championship for Makes was limited to 3-litre in engine capacity. So, no doubt to the relief of the Company's accountants, Porsche decided to withdraw temporarily from this expensive sport.

When the World Sports Car Championship, which had started in 1953, came to an end in 1961, the F.I.A. substituted two Championships, one for Prototype Sports Cars and the other for Grand Touring Cars. Prototype is something of a misnomer in this sense since the engineer has always used the name to mean the first-off of a new product which when fully tested and modified in the light of experience with this particular machine will eventually lead to a production model, the model that leaves the assembly line. To the F.I.A. the name Prototype has come to mean any experimental sports car made specially for competition. No more than one of the type need ever be made. The Grand Touring Group under the pressure of competition eventually spawned its own racing specialized GT cars and, despite the rule which at one time demanded that 100 of the vehicles to identical specification be made during the year, small specialist firms such as Ferrari and Maserati often flouted this rule. The C.S.I., whose duty it is to check that the required number of cars have actually been built, do occasionally have twinges of conscience, but this usually only leads to trouble. In 1964 for example they refused to homologate the Ferrari 250LM as a GT car since output had been too meagre. When the 275 GTB was also rejected Enzo Ferrari decided not to compete at all for the GT Championship until the C.S.I. saw fit to change the rules.

In 1973 there are three groups under which GT and sports cars can compete:

Group 3: Series Production Grand Touring Cars (Minimum Production 1000)
These are typical production GT cars with a minimum of 2 seats. Very few modifications are permitted to the manufacturer's specification and certainly nothing in the way of engine supertuning is permitted. 'Blueprinting', which is in effect the selective assembly of the engine, the matching (but not enlarging) of induction manifold ports to cylinder head ports, and any other careful and selective fitting of engine parts that does not modify them from specification, is permitted. Examples of this Group are the Lancia Fulvia Coupe and the Lotus Europa.

Group 4: Special Grand Touring Cars (Minimum production 500)
These are cars of more limited production (although the difference between 1000 and 500 seems hardly significant). The essential distinction from Group 3, however lies in the extent of the tuning permitted. For a full list of the permissions and exemptions the reader is referred to 'The F.I.A. Year Book of Automobile Sport' which is published every January and is obtainable in Great Britain from Patrick Stephens of 9 Ely Place, London, EC1. A summary of these permissible modifications is given in Appendix II in this book and apart from the retention of the main engine castings and the essential body parts a wide field of engine tuning and chassis tuning is permitted in this Group.

Group 5: Sports Cars
These are defined as two-seater competition cars manufactured specifically for speed or long-distance races on closed circuits. They must however carry 'all elements normally provided and legally required for vehicles using public roads'. A luggage compartment and spare wheel may however be omitted. Minimum cockpit dimensions are specified and certain external body dimensions are

controlled. Aerodynamic devices (i.e. aerofoils) may be attached to the body but the height and width are controlled (see Appendix II). A minimum weight is specified for each engine capacity.

The Canadian-American Challenge Cup

It is perhaps confusing to some that the Can-Am car which races in Group 7 and in many outward aspects is a two-seater racing sports car is described by the F.I.A. as a 'Two-Seater Racing Car'. It is not a sports car since it does not carry the legal requirements, such as lighting equipment, for use on the public roads but many of us would be inclined to ask 'and who would think of using Group 5 sports cars on the road even though they do barely comply with the law?'

The particular formula for Can-Am racing has grown out of the joint requirements of one large club, the Sports Car Club of America, of which the author was once happy to be a working member, and a group of Canadian motor clubs banded together under the title of the Canadian Automobile Sports Clubs. Racing is confined to selected circuits in the two countries and the vehicles, besides their nominal two seats, and open bodywork are oriented towards the use of the large capacity V-8 racing engines from Detroit. These engines are not by any means cheap but they are readily available and are certainly far less expensive than the slightly de-tuned Formula 1 engines that are used in Group 5 racing. There is no upper limit to engine size, nor is one restricted to the use of 'stock blocks' (the basic engine castings). Considerable re-working of stock blocks has been a way of life in all forms of motor racing in America for a generation at least and the popular engine today, the 495 cu. in Chevrolet (8.1 litres) when fitted with fuel injection will produce about 750 b.h.p. Oddly enough the most successful chassis for several years has been made by the McLaren Company, based in England, but with engines from their tune-shop in Detroit.

The Can-Am Series has been very successful and the author would welcome the news that some North American author is at work on the technical implications of this branch of motor sport. There are of course many common grounds to be found in the technology of motor sport and it is to be

hoped that many readers with interests as diverse as Formula
Vee and Rallycross will find something of value, something
to stimulate them intellectually, in this technical study of the
Racing Sports Car.

CHAPTER TWO
Tyres and Wheels

TYRES

One cannot proceed far in any design study of an automobile without discussing those four little areas of contact that the vehicle makes with the road surface. 'Little' did we say? A glance at Fig 2.1 shows what a change there has been in the size of these four areas of contact over half a century of motor racing. Fig 2.2 shows how the contact patch has increased in area since the twenties and the tyres shown in Fig 2.3, admittedly experimental in nature, seem to suggest we are moving towards a 90 per cent roller surface at the rear with a break in the middle for the drive!

To transmit torque to the road surface, to brake the car, to maintain a grip under centrifugal cornering forces those four contact patches must be held firmly to the road surface. This is the major function of the suspension system on a racing car. How this has become such a critical part of racing car design over the last ten to fifteen years will be the subject of the next chapter.

The Contact Patch and its Behaviour

The reader will have no doubt been made aware from his lighter reading in the motoring journals how these four contact patches, or 'footprints' as the American tyre men call them, control the direction of motion of a car after a change in the steering angle of the front wheels has been made, how the four tyres run at a slip-angle to exert side forces on the road surface and how the relative sizes of these slip angles at front and rear influence the general behaviour of a car. Tyres need not be pneumatic to exhibit the slip angle phenomena and one can use any model car, such as a 'Dinky' car, to see how a car understeers or oversteers. Even if you already know the mechanism it does give you an excuse to play with Junior's model cars while he is in bed.

Fig 2.1   Half a century of Dunlop racing tyres: Top row from the left:
Beaded edge (1920s); '5-stud' pattern (1930s); R1 (1946–58) R3
(1955–58); R4 (1956–58); R5 (1958–64). Bottom row from the left:
R6/CR48 (1963–65); R7/CR65 (1965–17); CR70 (1967); CR81–
special tyre for racing Minis (1968–72); CR82 (1968); CR84
(1969–71).

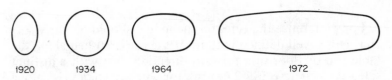

Fig 2.2   A history of change in contact patches.

Fig. 2.3   The rear tyre is the 1970–71 Can-Am (Group 7) racing tyre.
The front tyre, the ultimate so far in low-profile tyres, was produced
specially for the AFV Shadow Can-Am car that first raced in June 1970
at Mosport and was later destroyed in a road transporter accident. The
car used 10 inch diameter front wheels and 12 inch diameter rear
wheels.

For preference the tyres on the model should be fairly soft
and with a well defined pattern. If the car is pushed along the
table top or floor in a forward direction, but with a distinct
sideways bias (see Fig 2.4a) the car will move crabwise along
the surface, the extent of the side movement depending upon

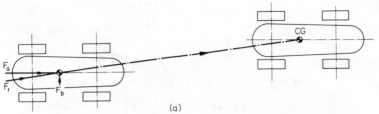

Fig 2.4a   Tyre side forces on model car–neutral steer.

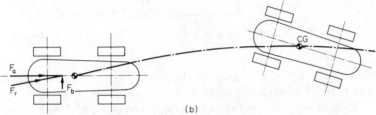

Fig 2.4b   Tyre side forces on model car–oversteer.

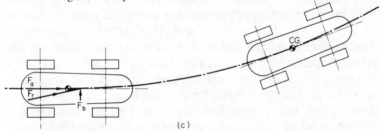

Fig 2.4c   Tyre side forces on model car–understeer.

the relative sizes of forces F_a and F_b. To maintain good contact with the table top there should also be a slight downward pressure to compensate for the lack of softness in the contact patch that is given on a normal car by the air in the tyre. Now let us try moving our finger more towards the rear of the model, so that the pressure acting downwards on the rear tyres is greater than that at the front. If we now also push forwards with a sideways bias, as in the first experiment, there will now be more slip on the rear tyres than on the front ones, as shown in Fig 2.4b and the car will exhibit the phenomenon we call oversteer, a subject we will discuss later. Moving the finger to a point forward of the centre of gravity will produce the opposite effect as shown in Fig 2.4c

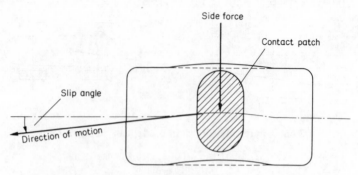

Fig 2.5   Wheel running at a slip angle to create a side force.

and when the slip angles on the front tyres exceed those at the rear we experience what we call understeer.

Considering the action of a single contact patch subjected to a side force as shown in simplified form in Fig 2.5 we see that each contact patch progresses along the road surface at an angle to the plane of the wheel. This angle is the slip angle. The manner in which the rubber elements that make up the tread or pattern resist this side force is a combination of a flexing and a scrubbing action. A perfectly smooth tread will also function if the rubber compound is soft enough and, as seen in the lower right-hand tyre of Fig 2.1 Dunlop had almost reached this stage in 1969 with their CR84 dry-weather tyre. With such a patternless tread however it is more than ever of vital importance to maintain an even pressure over the whole contact patch (but more of this and the way we achieve it when we discuss suspension systems). When a deep tread is used, as in wet-weather racing tyre, the CR88, (see Fig 2.6) the fairly deep flexible blocks of rubber are capable of a more independent action and each block or rib is flexed sideways as it enters the contact zone and is released as it leaves. Tyre wear on a normal road car is very much related to this scrubbing action as the elements that make up the tread pattern move against the road surface.

The Tyres and Stability

A car travelling in a vacuum on a perfectly level surface in a straight line would continue to do so with no call for steering

Fig 2.6   Dunlop CR88 wet-weather tyre. Note central drainage channel.

correction from the driver. As soon as we encounter road
surface irregularities, road camber or side winds the driver
finds it necessary to make small steering corrections even on
an apparently straight road. If we take Fig 2.4a to represent a
car subjected to a side force, such as might occur if a strong
gust of wind struck the side of the body, the slip angles
created in this way would be identical at front and rear and
the car, although displaced sideways would continue to travel
on a parallel line. This is called *neutral steer*. If however the

rear slip angles generated by the side force are greater than those generated at the front the car will start to follow a curved path, turning towards the disturbing force, as shown in Fig 2.4b. This is called *oversteer*. The effect of putting the car into this particular curving path is to generate a centrifugal force. acting at the centre of gravity of the car, which must be resisted by an increase in tyre forces at front and rear. The slip angles required to resist this new disturbance will again be greater at the rear than at the front. Thus if the driver does not take prompt corrective steering action the turning circle will get tighter and tighter, resulting finally in a spin. Oversteer may therefore be said to be an unstable condition. Fig 2.4c shows what happens in the opposite case of a car that has larger slip angles at the front than the rear when subjected to any disturbance. The car in this case turns away from the disturbing force. This is an *understeering* car and this may be said to be a stable condition since the curved path that the car has adopted introduces a centrifugal force that opposes the initial disturbing force. The car therefore has a natural tendency to run in a straight line. This as we will see later can at times be an embarrassment, but for the driver who tends to fall asleep at the wheel it does tend to prolong his life. Whether this is sociologically desirable is another matter.

Most car designers design understeer into their chassis for the straight-ahead condition. Unfortunately at high speeds aerodynamic effects begin to destroy the built-in understeer and at the speeds achieved by modern racing cars it is not always easy to design a body with a low drag that is also aerodynamically stable. The influence of aerodynamics on stability is discussed in Chapter Seven. Oversteer and understeer when cornering is again a subject on its own and is covered in Chapter Five.

The Limits of Tyre Adhesion

The contact patch of a tyre can exert forces up to a certain limiting point of adhesion in any direction, forwards during breaking or backwards for traction or sideways for cornering. When called upon to exert tractive effort or braking effort *at the same time* as cornering forces the limiting cornering force is reduced. A simple way to understand this is the concept of a 'circle of forces' as shown in Fig 2.7. This is a simplification, however, and all tread patterns do not conform precisely to this simple rule. As an extreme example, the old ribbed motor-cycle tyres which were designed expressly to

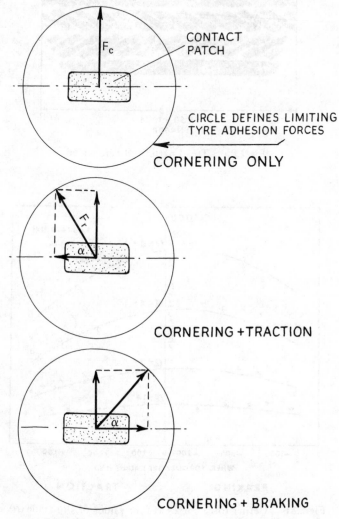

Fig 2.7   The Circle of Forces: how available cornering force is reduced during traction and braking.

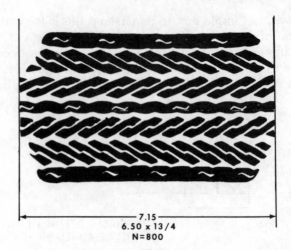

Fig 2.8a   Tread pattern of tyre tested.

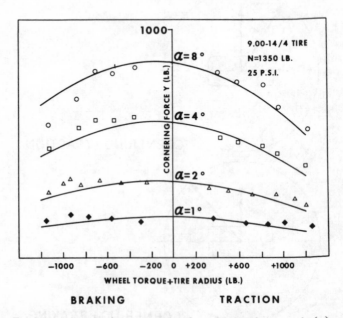

Fig 2.8b   Corner force curves at four values of slip angle (α).
After J. R. Nothstine and F. N. Beauvis, Ford Motor Co.

give excellent cornering would not exert the same forces
during traction and braking. A modern racing tyre, however, behaves fairly closely to this concept. The circle
defines the limiting force that the contact patch will exert on
the road surface under some particular conditions (i.e. dry,
slightly damp, wet, etc.) If the car is cornering without
traction or braking the limiting cornering force is represented
by the radius of the circle, F_c as shown in the first diagram (a).
When braking or accelerating the resultant of the two forces
$F_r = F_c$ = the radius, but the component available for exerting the cornering force is reduced to $F_c \sin \alpha$. By opening the
throttle when cornering at high slip angles a driver can
increase the slip angles at the driving wheels, unless he is
already running at the limiting adhesion value for the
conditions, when of course he would just induce a slide. On a
front wheel drive car the use of traction in a bend will tend
to make the car run wide (understeer) on a rear wheel drive
car it will cause the rear slip angles to increase relative to the
front, i.e. to oversteer.

Good corroborative evidence of the above theory was
given by some experiments carried by the Ford Motor
Company in Detroit. The particular tyre under test was a
9.00 x 14 casing as used on a full size sedan. The tyre
pressure was 24 lb/in² and the vertical load was 1350 lb. The
contact patch shown in Fig. 2.8 shows the tread pattern and the
loss of cornering force when braking or traction is applied to
the wheel is clearly demonstrated by the graphs in Fig 2.8b.
The loss appears to be much greater at greater slip angles. A
slip angle of 8° would be high for a passenger car, but racing
cars sometimes run at slip angles in the region of 12° to 14°,
where even a small loss in cornering power can be most
critical.

Improving the Grip
The high degree of resilience exhibited by cured rubber
together with an ability to adapt its shape to irregularities in
the road surface contributes to the extraordinary grip that a
modern tyre can exert on a dry surface. Even on a wet
surface the wiping action of a good design of tread makes

rubber superior to any other commercially available substances. There is of course half a century of experimentation with the chemistry of rubber manufacture and the allied synthetic compounds that are now used. Since the writer is neither polymer chemist nor rubber technologist it is perhaps fortunate that the subject is too vast for us to attempt anything more than a sketchy outline. Sulphur is traditionally added in controlled quantities to natural rubber to modify the molecular structure under the action of heat in the process we call vulcanization, or curing. Uncured rubber is just a sticky dough-like material lacking in resilience. Oil and carbon black are also added to improve the resistance to abrasion. Other additives in small quantities assist the vulcanization process, others help to increase the length of the molecular chains, other improve resistance to sunlight and the atmosphere. How many of the tyre companies have secret ingredients we can only surmise. Making a guess based on many other products, we would say it is more likely to be in the quantities used that they vary. They are certainly most unwilling to disclose any exact figures on rubber mixes.

Wet-Weather Tyres
Dunlop introduced a wet weather tyre in 1963 which gave a much improved grip on the road in wet conditions than had ever been achieved before. The rubber mix used contained large amounts of a synthetic rubber that is usually called a 'high μ (mu)' compound. Mu is the tyre technologists symbol for hysteresis and in this context high hysteresis means that the rubber, after compression at the contact patch, does not restore all the energy of compression; the higher the hysteresis value, the higher the amount of energy converted into heat. A tyre with a high-mu tread compound should therefore not run for long on a hot dry road at racing speeds. It is just one of the unhappy facts of life for a team manager that the only material available to give a good grip on the road in wet conditions will run dangerously hot under dry conditions. Today he has a third choice available since intermediate compounds are available and intermediate tread patterns, but the fact remains that a race is often decided by the choice of tyres before the start.

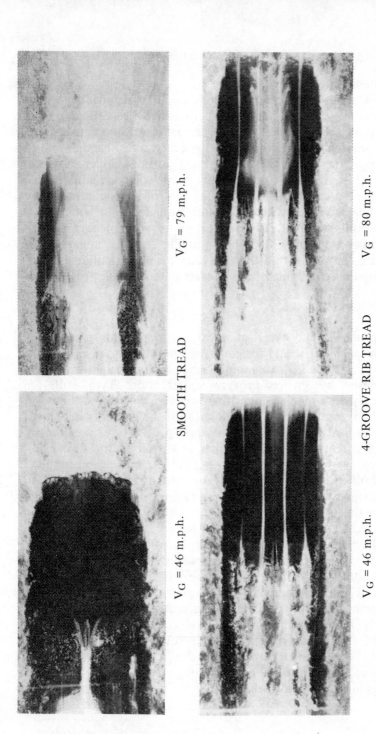

V_G = 46 m.p.h.   SMOOTH TREAD V_G = 79 m.p.h.

V_G = 46 m.p.h.   4-GROOVE RIB TREAD V_G = 80 m.p.h.

Fig 2.9 Aquaplaning—Comparison of water flow under smooth and 4-groove rib tread tires at speeds of 46 and approaching 80 m.p.h. Vertical Load=835lb; tire pressure=27lb/in^2; water depth=0.02 inch.

Aquaplaning

In America the phenomenon is called hydroplaning and it occurs at speed on very wet roads when the particular tread pattern is such that it fails to remove the water film striking the leading edge of the contact patch at a fast enough rate to prevent the tyre from 'water-skiing' in the manner shown in Fig 2.9. Dunlop found that deep wide circumferential grooves prevent this build-up of hydrodynamic pressure by passing large quantities of water from front to back across the contact patch. In their ultimate, very successful, wet-weather tyre, the CR88 shown in Fig 2.6, they removed the entire centre-rib from the tyre to give a massive drainage path along the centre-line of the contact patch.

WHEELS

The wheels and tyres of a car are the major part of the unsprung weight and for good road holding it is essential that this weight be kept to a minimum. This low weight cannot be achieved by savings in tyre construction. Tyre walls are already very much thinner than we once considered the norm and any reduction in the thickness of the crown (where most of the material is on an extra-low profile tyre) would only reduce the tread life. Titanium is now used for suspension arms, even for the coil springs, and the suspension uprights and other castings and forgings are usually in aluminium alloy or magnesium. The wheels on a racing sports car are so wide now that a substantial saving in weight can be made by using the right materials and the right design.

There was a time when the centre-lock wire wheel was the only wheel to be considered for racing and sports cars. It was, of course, the lightest production wheel available before the war. The experience of Ettore Bugatti serves to illustrate this, since he abandoned his famous aluminium alloy wheels (of a fairly low-strength alloy by modern standards) which had eight flat radial spokes when he designed the Type 59 in 1933. These new wire wheels on the Type 59 were made with a large number of fine gauge steel spokes and were 2lb lighter than his earlier alloy wheels.

Today the choice for a competition vehicle lies between aluminium alloy or magnesium alloy in cast form. Light weight is not the only advantage of the alloy wheel. It is more rigid than the pressed-steel wheel and very much more rigid than the wire wheel. The die-cast magnesium alloy wheel is undoubtedly the lightest available in Europe, being about 12 per cent lighter on average than the best aluminium alloy wheels. The corrosion failure risk is much higher though with magnesium. It is essential to keep the surface painted. Even the careless use of tyre levers can damage the resin protective coating and deposit steel particles that will set up electrolytic corrosion of the exposed magnesium. Corrosion pits can be started in this way that can lead to fatigue failure. Regular crack- testing is the only safe-guard, but this presents no problems to the professionally-managed racing team.

An alternative to cast wheels is now available in America where Chassis Engineering of National City, California, are making a very light aluminium wheel fabricated by welding. These are claimed to be lighter than cast magnesium wheels but the author has no experience of them.

The pattern for the future appears to be as follows:—

1. small diameter wheels with a deep enough rim designed to prevent over-riding of the tyre bead under cornering accelerations especially when tyre pressure is below normal (slow puncture).
2. The wheel rim must be of sufficient width to match the tyre width. Wide tyres on narrow rims lack stability when cornering.
3. The maintenance of correct tyre pressure, especially as the air inside the tyre gradually increases in temperature during the early laps of a race, will become a serious problem when tyre profiles are reduced still further. There is only one pressure that gives a perfectly flat contact patch and an increase of as little as 2 lb/in^2 in tyre pressure can cause sufficient convexity to reduce the contact patch to a large extent. Special tyre valves that blow off surplus pressure as the tyre warms up would be a partial solution. Another would be a special design of wheel incorporating

Fig 2.10   Uninflated racing tyre–Dunlop CR84.

internal tubes for topping up or bleeding off small high
pressure nitrogen bottles. If tyres of the profile ratio
shown in Fig. 2.3 ever become popular some automatic
control of tyre pressure will no doubt be developed. The
concavity of an uninflated racing tyre is shown in Fig.
2.10.

CHAPTER THREE

The Suspension

MODERN TRENDS

Modern tyre developments have dramatically changed all suspension requirements, so much so that many types of suspension have become obsolete in a single decade. The Porsche trailing link system, for example, which was so successful on the Aston Martins in the Fifties, gives such a large change in camber angle with roll as to make the system completely unacceptable for low profile racing tyres. Of the orthodox suspension systems only four remain to be considered and the first of these listed below is the one in almost universal use today on racing cars:–

(a) unequal-length double wishbones, sometimes triangulated in plan to resist traction and braking torques and often supplemented by single or double parallel longitudinal torque tubes. This system is shown as a line diagram defining the roll-centre in Fig. 3.1 and with more detail in Fig. 3.2. The Bobsy racing sports car, designed by Jerry Mong of Vanguard Automotive Enterprises of Medina, Ohio, to compete in SCCA Class C sports car events, is used to illustrate typical examples of this form of suspension. Fig 3.3 show the front suspension with direct action on the coil spring/damper unit. Fig 3.4 is of the rear suspension (the drive shaft and one upper

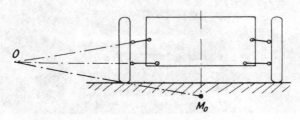

Fig 3.1   Unequal length double wishbone suspension.

41

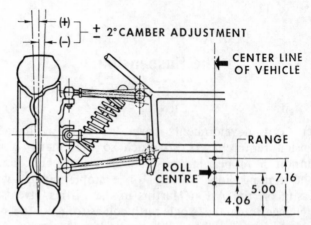

Fig 3.2   Example of double wishbone system; rear suspension on Mustang Mark 1.

Fig 3.3   Front suspension on Bobsy racing sports car (SCCA Class C).

Fig 3.4   Rear suspension on Bobsy racing sports car.

suspension link being removed to give a clearer view of the variable-rate spring operation). This rocking lever is a popular device to make the suspension gradually increase in stiffness as full bump (upward compression) is reached. As the right-hand side of the lever rises the leverage changes, reaching maximum stiffness when the fulcrum and the spring attachment pin are horizontal.

(b) the De Dion axle, shown in Fig 3.5 and 3.6, can be regarded as a cross between independent rear suspension and the traditional beam axle, but this is not strictly

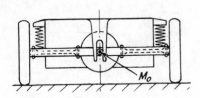

Fig 3.5   De Dion suspension in outline.

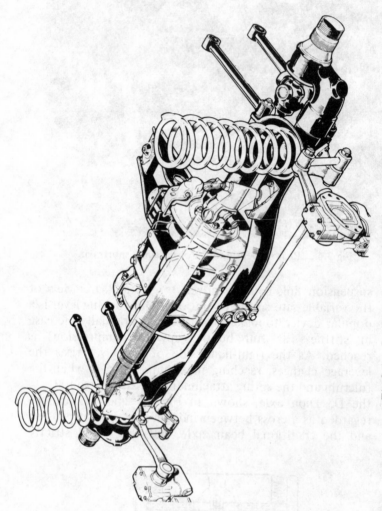

Fig 3.6   De Dion rear suspension on Aston Martin DBS.

correct since the two wheels cannot move independently
The wheel hub-carriers are connected by a light transverse beam, usually circular in cross-section and this
member is usually given lateral location relative to the
chassis by a simple A-bracket attached to the centre or
by means of a Watt's parallel motion linkage. The drive
mechanism resembles that used in an independent rear
suspension system. The final drive box is mounted on the
chassis and flexible drive shafts take the drive to each
wheel. Since the distance between wheel centres remains
constant, but the drive lengths vary under suspension
movement a splined connection is necessary at some
point such as the inner universal joint.

(c) the Chapman (or Macpherson) strut uses a long suspension strut incorporating the coil spring and damper unit,
a fore and aft link to resist traction and braking torques
and the flexible drive shaft (with no splined connection)
to act as a control link on the lateral location of the hub
carrier. Good examples are given in Fig 3.7 and 3.21.

(d) the conventional beam axle, lightened by the use of
modern materials, is surprisingly enough, a type of
suspension system that has been under review in recent
years (see Fig 3.8) since it offers a solution to the
problem of maintaining zero wheel camber on both inner
and outer wheels in a corner. Wheel camber will also not
change when both wheels on the same axle rise and fall
when traversing a ridge in the road surface, but a fairly
large change in camber will occur on both wheels when
only one of them rides over a bump or a hollow.

Suspension Terminology

Many readers will be familiar with such terms as roll centre,
camber, etc., but a few definitions will help at this stage.

Bump (Jounce in the U.S.A.) is the upward movement of a
wheel from the static loaded position, thus compressing the
spring.

Rebound is movement of the wheel in the opposite direction
to Bump. It occurs under the natural tendency of the loaded

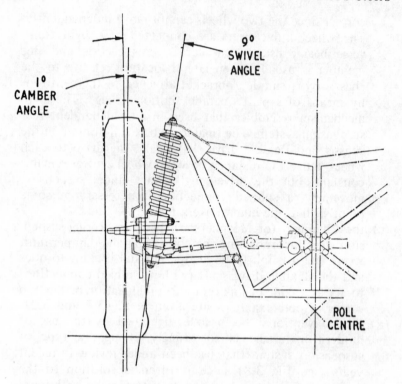

Fig 3.7   Chapman Strut suspension.

spring to overshoot its static position when recovering from bump. It can also occur when a wheel drops into a depression in the road surface.

Pitching is a fore and aft rocking motion, alternately compressing the front springs, i.e. putting both into bump, while the rear springs are extended, or in rebound, then reversing the spring movements. The time for a complete fore and aft oscillstion of the body on its springs is controlled by the spring rates (i.e. the natural oscillating frequency of front and rear springs in number of oscillations per minute) and by the inertia of the masses that go to make up the whole sprung structure.

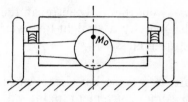

Fig 3.8   Beam axle.

Roll is angular rotation of the sprung mass in the transverse plane, i.e. at right-angles to the movement of pitching.

Roll-centre is the point in the transverse plane of the front wheel contact patches, or the rear contact patches, about which the sprung mass of the car will rotate under any disturbing force.

Roll-steer is a transient effect on the path followed by a car in a bend. Thus a car with a high roll-centre at the rear and much of the weight aft will suffer more weight transfer from the inner to the outer wheel at the rear than at the front. This will lead to an oversteering effect. There is always a lag, since the inertia of the unsprung mass resists this action. A car with its mass concentrated towards the CG may still exhibit roll steer, since the relative softness of the front and rear suspensions is involved, but the response will be almost immediate. A large sedan with large masses concentrated at relatively large distances from the CG and with the customary soft springing all round will have a lag of as much as two seconds before the full effects of roll-steer occur when negotiating a chicane. In such a case the body can still be exerting roll-steer to the right after the steering wheel has been turned to negotiate the left-hand section of the chicane. For a time the roll-steer effect tends to negate the steering demand from the steering angle applied to the front wheels. The subject is fraught with mathematics and in the remit of this book it is enough if the reader appreciates that roll in itself can induce more or less understeer, or oversteer and that the effect is not instantaneous.

Roll Axis. If we join the roll-centre at the front and the roll-centre at the rear by a straight-line we have drawn the roll-axis of the sprung mass.

Anti-roll Bars are transverse bars, cranked at each end, that are attached to some convenient point on the suspension links, such as a wishbone arm. They can be fitted either to the front suspension or the rear suspension and the effect is a stiffening of the suspension under rolling conditions, as in a fast corner. When both wheels at the same end of the car rise or fall together the anti-roll bar is not under torsion; when cornering the outer wheel bends the cranked end upwards and the inner wheel bends it downwards. The use of an anti-roll bar depends very much on the cornering behaviour of a particular car. As a general rule we tend to find one fitted to the more heavily loaded end of a car.

Wheel Camber is inclination of the plane of the wheel to the vertical. It is conventionally called positive when the top of the tyre is at a greater distance from the vertical centre plane of the car when static than the bottom of the tyre. Positive and negative camber of 2° is shown in Fig 3.2

The Design Parameters for Unequal-Length Double Wishbones

The use of short upper wishbones or triangulated links and longer lower links, often with a single or two parallel longitudinal torque rods resist the torque imposed by traction or braking, has become an almost universal system. The system is light and lends itself to simple design changes and can only be challenged by the Chapman strut system for the ultimate in lightness.

The following design parameters are available to make changes in the position of the roll-centre and to influence the camber changes under bump and rebound:—

(a) the relative lengths of the links
(b) the ratio of link length to track
(c) the angles the links make to the horizontal
(d) the relative angles between the upper and lower links.

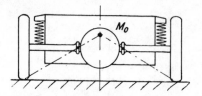

Fig 3.9   Swing axle suspension.

By ringing the changes on these four parameters we can make wide changes in roll-centre height, camber change, track variation, etc. The availability of a computer is almost a necessity to the suspension designer today.

The angle between the upper and lower links determines what is called the 'effective swing-axle length'. A true swing-axle is shown diagrammatically in Fig 3.9. If the upper and lower links of a wishbone system are placed at a large angle, as in Fig 3.10 the effective swing-axle length can be seen to be short. In Fig 3.11, where they are almost parallel, the effective swing-axle length is large. Early designs of wishbone suspension, such as on the R Type MG Midget, had parallel equal length links (see Fig 3.12) and the effective swing-axle length was therefore infinite. The position of the instantaneous roll-centre is determined from the intersection of two lines as shown in Figs 3.10 and 3.11. Point X is the point on the road surface where the axis of the wishbone outer pivots intersects. A line is drawn from this point to the effective swing-axle pivot Y. The *instantaneous* roll-centre of

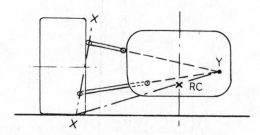

Fig 3.10   Double wishbone suspension with short effective swing axle radius.

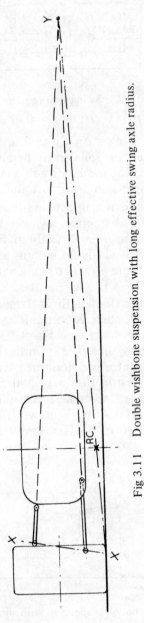

Fig 3.11   Double wishbone suspension with long effective swing axle radius.

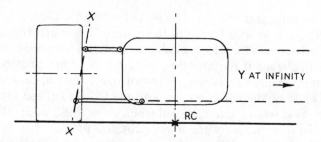

Fig 3.12   Double wishbone suspension with infinite effective swing axle radius.

the sprung mass (i.e. the body/chassis) is point RC on the centre-line of the car. This point RC can rise or fall under the action of body roll in some cases, hence the use of the term 'instantaneous'.

Roll Resistance
By variations in the link lengths and angles, i.e. the four parameters (a), (b), (c) and (d) it is possible to produce wide changes in the position of the roll-centre and in the camber angle changes under bump and rebound. It is obvious that a high roll-centre will reduce the angle of roll for a given cornering acceleration. This can be demonstrated by reference to Fig 3.13. On the parallel link IFS system shown at (a) the rolling moment during cornering is $\mu W_s h_1$ where μ is the centrifugal acceleration in gravities, W_s is the sprung mass and

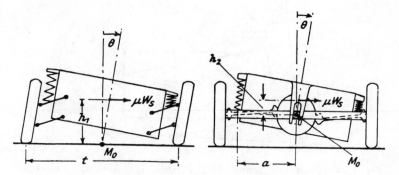

Fig 3.13   Roll Moments on wishbone and De Dion suspensions.

h_1 is the roll-centre height. In case (b) with a De Dion axle the roll-centre is at axle level and the value of h is much reduced. Roll resistance is therefore much greater with a high roll-centre.

At this stage it requires no great amount of imagination to ask the pertinent question: Why not make the roll-centres at both ends of the car coincide with the CG axis of the sprung mass? This would give zero roll when cornering. An excellent idea and one that we were able to put into practice before the introduction of independent suspension when roll-centre heights were naturally high. As shown in Fig 3.14 it is easy enough to get a high roll-centre by suitable inclination of the links, but this introduces undesirable camber changes when a

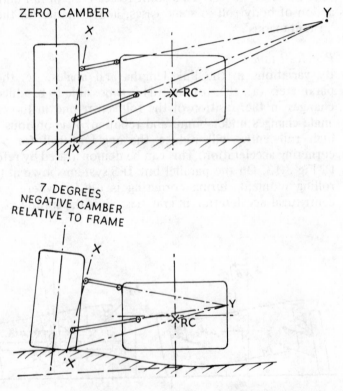

Fig 3.14   High roll centre with unequal length double wishbone system. Effect of road surface irregularities.

single wheel rises and falls on a ripply surface. If, for example, the vehicle was negotiating a fast bend when the outer wheel passed over such a large ripple in the road surface the tyre contact patch would almost be reduced to a tiny area at the inner shoulder. This could have disastrous consequences. If we change the lengths of the wishbone, making the upper links longer than the lower, while maintaining a high pivot for the effective swing-axle, a similar unacceptable change in camber angle will occur when a single wheel drops into a hollow in the road.

Gyroscopic Effects
Keeping the whole of the contact patch pressed firmly on the road surface, whatever the contours of that surface (within reasonable limits!) is well established as a prime requirement for the suspension geometry of a racing car. This demands a camber change from full bump to full rebound that does not exceed plus or minus as little as 1° in the case of the latest low-profile tyres. Let us suppose, however, that the tyre men at some time in the future present us with a new concept in tyres that is not so sensitive to camber changes. There would still remain one aspect of camber change that is undesirable. This is the aspect of gyroscopic torque created when a spinning wheel has its axis of rotation changed. Let us consider that Fig 3.14 represents a front view of a racing car in the middle of a fast corner. If the outer wheel is suddenly bounced upwards by the road surface and, from the particularly undesirable suspension geometry shown, the outer wheel is then given a negative camber of at least 5° (actually 7° as drawn) the sudden change in the axis of spin will introduce fairly large gyroscopic steering moments. A moment will be exerted at the wheel hub to try to steer the particular wheel towards a greater turning radius. A camber change in the opposite direction would have the opposite steering effect. A camber change on a rear wheel will of course not be felt at the steering wheel but the gyroscopic forces generated by large camber changes on the rear wheels will be fed back into the suspension mountings and the rear wheel steering effects will still influence the path of the car, just as a gust of wind on the rear end of an estate car will put a driver off his chosen line.

A Contemporary System

The Porsche 917 suspension geometry, as shown in Figs 3.15 and 3.16, represents the best 'conventional' thinking. At the end of the chapter we will discuss briefly a few less conventional ideas. The first thing we notice is that the front and rear geometry are not quite alike. At the rear there is an additional constraint on the geometry. Unless sliding type

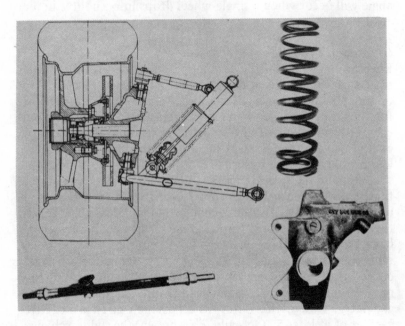

Fig 3.15   Front suspension on Porsche 917.

(pot-joints) universal joints are incorporated in the drives to the rear wheels it is advisable to place the inboard pivots of the upper and lower links on a line that passes through the centre of the rubber-bushed splined coupling (shown in Fig 3.16). Splines tend to introduce an unpredictable amount of friction into the suspension system. By placing the splined connection at this point the amount of 'spline-pumping' with suspension move-

ment is reduced to a minimum. The actual drive shaft assembly
(seen at the bottom of Fig 3.16) has a Hooke's type universal
joint at each end and a rubber-bushed coupling to absorb
torque variations.

Returning to the comparison between the front and the rear
suspension geometries it is apparent that the effective

Fig 3.16   Rear suspension on Porsche 917.

swing-axle pivot is higher at the rear and the roll-centre is well
above ground level (about 2.5 inches above). At the front the
instantaneous roll-centre is about 0.5 inches below ground
level. The roll axis (Fig 3.17) is therefore inclined upwards to
the rear and for a very good reason. One can consider the roll
moment *under steady state constant radius cornering conditions* as those represented in Fig 3.17 where the roll moment

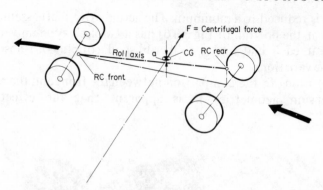

Fig 3.17   Roll Axis geometry.

acting on the springs is the product of force F and height a. In a typical corner however there is usually a variation in the cornering forces and there is always a transitional phase at the start of a corner when the body has not yet reached its equilibrium roll angle and a transitional phase leaving the corner when the roll tends to lag behind the actual cornering forces. How a car behaves under these transitional and variable g-force conditions is influenced very much by the disposition of the main sprung masses and the inclination of the roll axis.

    The main sprung masses in the Porsche 917 have a bias towards the rear. Moreover the masses towards the rear are appreciably higher than those at the front, the engine and transaxle being largely responsible for this. We can treat the mass distribution in terms of a series of thin slices running from the front to the back, each slice having its own centre of mass or centroid. By joining all these centroids by a line running from end to end we obtain the *mass centroid line* shown in Fig 3.18. This will not be a straight line but to simplify the analysis a little we have reduced this to a simple straight axis as shown in Fig 3.19 with the masses concentrated into two parts, M_f and M_r on the front and rear wheel hub planes. The Porsche design team have chosen a roll axis which is approximately parallel with this centroid axis. Let us consider what would happen with a roll axis parallel to the ground as shown in the figure. When entering a corner the

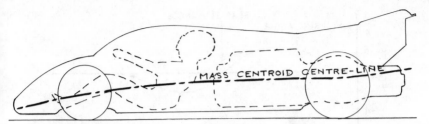

Fig 3.18   Effective mass distribution in vertical plane.

roll moment at the rear would be very much greater than at the front. Not only is M_r greater than M_f, but the arm through which it acts, a_r is greater than a_f. The spring rates at the rear can be made much higher than at the front; the front springs can be fitted with an anti-roll bar but these are only palliatives. The good engineering solution is to balance the roll moments at front and rear by inclining the roll-axis. This is the solution adopted by Porsche.

Slalom Turns

The behaviour of a car in 'wiggle-woggle' or slalom turn manoeuvres depends largely upon two factors the degree of understeer or oversteer and the amount of roll-steer present. It is a very complex problem and suspension engineers have been

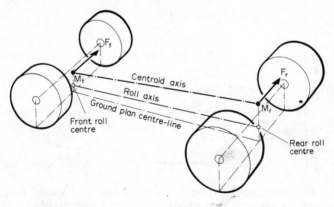

Fig 3.19   Relationship of Centroid Axis to Roll Axis.

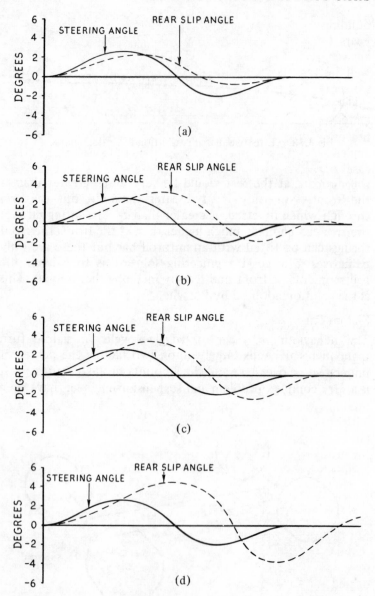

Fig 3.20 Influence of roll-steer on behaviour in a slalom turn: (a) understeering car with negligible roll-steer, (b) understeering car with pronounced roll-steer, (c) oversteering car with negligible roll-steer,(d) oversteering car with pronounced roll-steer.

building up a bank of information on the subject over many years that will eventually give them the ideal computerized answer. To indicate the types of behaviour to be expected from well-defined characteristics Fig 3.20 has been drawn in which we see how the rear slip angles can be expected to respond to the steering angles during a slalom turn for four particular cars. Only rear slip angles are shown for simplicity. It will be realized however that in the case of the understeering car the front slip angles will be larger than the rear slip angles and smaller in the case of the oversteering vehicle. A study of these graphs suggests that a car with oversteer and a large measure of rear roll-steer will be a tricky vehicle to put through a chicane with any degree of control or accuracy. Not only does the car over-respond to the steering input, but the car is still steering to the left long after the driver has turned the wheel to the right. Removal of the roll-steer from both understeering and oversteering vehicles gives what appears to be an acceptable steering response. This is supported by much recent research in handling characteristics. The understeering car, however, must have only a small degree of understeer; one with a high degree of understeer has a tendency to demolish the chicane when taken at speed.

Dr Hans Mezger, who was responsible for the design team that produced the Type 917, was very conscious of the need to minimize unsprung weight. Where possible he chose materials with the highest specific strength (strength/weight ratio). Other considerations sometimes take precedence. Brake discs, for instance, cannot be made of a light material since cast-iron is the only known material that can resist the abrasive action of the brake pads and at the same time give an acceptable wear life to the pads themselves. The discs on the Porsche 917 are of ventilated construction (with internal radial blades like a fan) but the weight of the disc alone is far in excess of all the other metal components in the wheel and suspension assembly. The disc is mounted on a forged aluminium alloy bell, suitably drilled for lightness, as can be seen top right in Fig 3.16. The front and rear wheel hubs are machined from a titanium alloy of tensile strength in the range 60-75 ton/in^2 and titanium alloys of the same high strength are used for the housings of the outer ball pivots on the suspension links and for the rack and pinion steering gears. Magnesium alloy castings are used for the road wheels, the suspension uprights (the hollow casting at the bottom right of Fig 3.16) and for the rack and pinion housing (bottom left of Fig 3.15).

The suspension springs are of titanium for lightness and strength. To provide a variable rate spring, one with an increasing rate under deflection, the bar from which the spring is made is ground with a slight taper before the spring is wound. The suspension links, including the longitudinal torque-- resisting links, which are not visible in the cross-sectional views, are made from solid-drawn high-tensile aluminium alloy tubing. The ends are tapered and threaded to take the pivot housings. The inner pivots are spherical bearings with Teflon bushes and titanium housings. The outer pivots are of similar construction materials and are provided with an adjustment to facilitate accurate setting up of the suspension geometry. When such small variations in camber make such a difference to the dynamic behaviour it is essential to remove all sources of free play and to minimize distortion in components. The produc- tion engineer can cover up the accumulative errors caused by wide tolerances and sloppy assembly-line techniques by using rubber bushes at strategic points in the suspension system. Such devices are anathema to the racing car designer and would certainly be a positive danger when low profile tyres are used.

Alternative Suspension Systems

The Beam Axle

The traditional beam axle can no longer be considered for the driven end of a racing car (the rear end in the contemporary racing sports car). With a live axle containing the weight of the final drive gears and differential components, even the use of titanium for the gears and magnesium alloy for the castings, would leave us with a very bouncing and rocking lump of metal connecting the two wheel hubs together. The inertia would be such that single wheel bump or rebound would give large and undesirable camber changes to both rear wheels. Experiments on a beam axle have been rumoured at the Lotus Works and these, presumably, have been directed at the production of an ultra-light front beam axle in magnesium alloy or titanium. Camber control would be

excellent on a good surface but would be mediocre on a
rough one. The roll-centre would be high and could even be
above the CG line at the front. Some modification of the
normal beam axle has probably been invented by the bright
young men at Wymondham and it would be unwise to
anticipate their thoughts.

The De Dion Axle
The De Dion axle separates the two functions of the
orthodox beam-type rear axle. The two wheels are held
rigidly parallel by a light beam, usually tubular, which in turn
is located by a Watt's linkage or similar system. The final
drive box is not part of the unsprung weight, as in the simple
beam axle, but is mounted on the frame, universally-jointed
drive shafts being used to take the drive to the two wheels in
the manner of an independent rear suspension. The unsprung
weight is appreciably heavier than an IRS system and the
interaction between the rigidly connected wheels would show
up to great disadvantage using low-profile racing tyres on a
poorly surfaced road such as the Madonie Circuit of the
Targa Florio. For the Le Mans De Dion suspension might still
be acceptable. It would certainly be more rugged than many
of the spidery wishbones that collapse from time to time in
racing today.

The Chapman Strut
The Chapman strut (or MacPherson strut as the Ford Motor
Company call it) was convincingly demonstrated on the
Lotus Elite and Elan as a very effective light suspension
system. Fig 3.21 shows the rear suspension on the Lotus
Elite, the all-fibreglass fore-runner of the Elan. In studying
this system it is important to observe that the outer sliding
portion of the strut is integral with the hub carrier. The
upper end of the rod member is attached to the frame
through a rubber bush which allows a small degree of angular
movement. The damper elements are incorporated in the
strut and the coil spring is located on the outside. The
required geometry necessitates a long strut and this cannot
usually be incorporated in low open racing sports cars.
Where a GT body is fitted the necessary length can usually

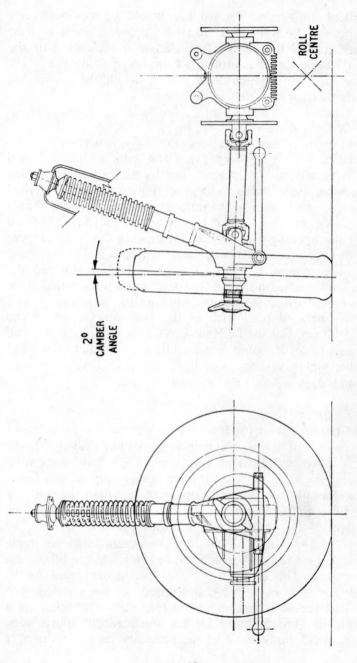

ROLL CENTRE

2° CAMBER ANGLE

Fig 3.21 Chapman Strut on Lotus Elite.

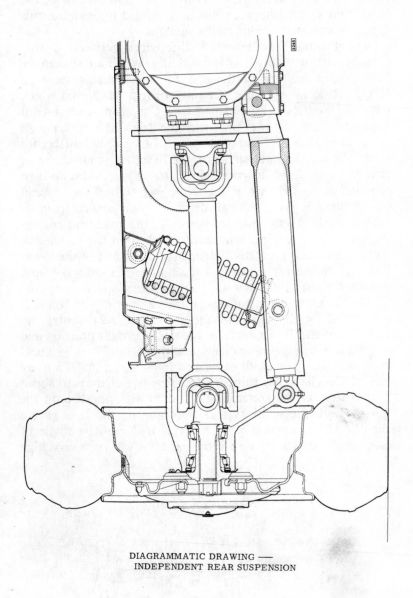

DIAGRAMMATIC DRAWING —
INDEPENDENT REAR SUSPENSION

Fig 3.22   Rear suspension on E Type Jaguar.

be incorporated at the rear. Profiles are now so low at the front that Colin Chapman has been forced to abandon this type of suspension on his racing vehicles.

To illustrate the essential differences between a true Chapman strut suspension and a double wishbone system we have used a drawing of the E Type Jaguar rear suspension (Fig 3.22) as an example of a modern rear suspension which bears a superficial resemblance to a Chapman strut since it appears to have a lower link, with the drive shaft acting as an upper link, as in the Chapman design. The essential difference is as follows: the hub carrier on the Elite (and, indeed, on all strut-type designs, is constrained to move in bump and rebound along the axis of the strut, even though the top end of the strut is given a small degree of compliance from its rubber bush. In the Jaguar, however, the twin coil spring/ damper units are placed in front and behind the lower link and are attached pivotally towards the outer end of the lower link and to the car frame and the hub carrier can take up a different angle from that adopted by the suspension spring.

On the Chapman strut design the camber of the wheel is controlled by the angle of the strut. Fig 3.21 shows the position of the Roll Centre in the static upright position and Fig 3.23, which is purely diagrammatic, shows how the wheel camber changes on both outer and inner wheel under a body roll of 6°. The static camber of 2° negative changes to about 4° positive on the outer wheel and to 4½° negative on the inner wheel. Since the tyre section used on the Elite gave a slightly higher cornering force at a small positive angle of camber the cornering power on the Elite was of a very high

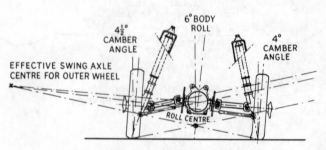

Fig 3.23   Effect of roll on Lotus Elite at rear.

order. The fall in the level of the instantaneous roll-centre is a distinct disadvantage with this system, since the roll moment increases with increasing roll. Fairly stiff suspension is therefore advisable when using a Chapman strut system.

Unconventional Designs

Anti-dive and Anti-squat

Dive is best demonstrated on an older type of American sedan with worn dampers. Under hard braking the front end of the car dips and the rear end rises. If the car ahead or behind performed the same curtsy it was not uncommon at one time to see them immobilized with bumpers locked, for all the world like stags in the rutting season. Detroit when pushed will always find a solution and the anti-dive suspensions which are used on modern American cars have the upper and lower suspension pivots set at an angle where they are attached to the frame. Lines drawn through these four attachments converge at a point several feet behind the front wheels. The effect of this is to make a component of the braking torque feed back an upward thrust into the front suspension which counterbalances the downward rocking action of the body on its springs.

Racing cars, for reasons which will be discussed in Chapter Seven, are designed with an extremely small ground clearance. The F.I.A. minimum of 10 cm (3.94 inches is seldom exceeded in the static position. With tyre adhesion coefficients now as high as 1.4 g and front brakes designed to take advantage of this phenomenal grip on the road it is not surprising, despite the hard suspensions to see some cars grounding the front edges of the bodywork under hard braking. What is sometimes regarded as of more consequence is the opposite effect when a car tends to squat, i.e. sit down at the rear end, during fierce acceleration since this can upset the wheel cambers at the rear and reduce the effective area of the rear contact patches. Unfortunately the experimental installations tried on GP cars during 1971 were found to have undesirable side-effects on the general handling of the car and Lotus, among others, abandoned the anti-squat layout in their Formula 1 suspension.

Fig 3.24   The Kolbe 'Curvebank' car (standard Chevrolet on the right).

The Kolbe Curve-Bank Car

The author first encountered this novel suspension in 1961 when he drove a Chevrolet sedan converted to lean inwards, or *bank* when turning a normal flat corner. Joachim Kolbe of Menomonee Falls, Winsconsin had been working for about twenty years on banking car bodies and his original patents have probably now expired. The 1961 Chevrolet Impala conversion was well engineered and the handling was much improved over the stock car. The two cars in Fig 3.24 are taking identical curves at the same speed, turning to the driver's left. The body roll on the stock Impala on the right is an angle of about 6°. On the Kolbe curve-bank car the body is rolling inwards at an angle of about 2.5° and the outer front wheel has a slight negative camber. The Kolbe suspension system could be set up to have zero banking in a turn and what is perhaps of more interest to us in the context of this book it could be developed to maintain zero camber on both inner and outer wheels at high cornering acceleration. In its stage of development when tested by the author the Kolbe conversion was very heavy, but a much lighter system could no doubt be devised when designing *ab initio*.

The Trebron DRC Suspension

Norbert Hamy, a Canadian architect with a keen interest in motor racing, invented the Trebron Double Roll-Centre (DRC) suspension about five years ago with the sole object of eliminating body roll and wheel camber change during cornering on racing cars. The Trebron chassis uses two roll-centres, one at ground level for the wheels, which have parallel *equal length* wishbones and one, shown at RC_2 in Fig 3.25, for the body. To hold the wheels upright in a turn Norbert Hamy uses the centrifugal force acting on the body to rotate the suspension location links attached to the inner pivots of the upper suspension arms in a direction that maintains wheel verticality within less than ¼° of variation. In Fig 3.26 it is seen that the body has rolled about its high roll-centre, RC_2 by only 1° under the action of 1.4 G centrifugal acceleration. The sprung bulkhead, however, which only absorbs lateral suspension loads, has rolled through 3.5°. The differing inclinations of the two suspension location links when cornering should be noted. The energy to move the inner pivots of the upper suspension arms relative to the sprung bulkhead all comes from a sideways shift of the body under the centrifugal force. Fig 3.27 shows in a schematic manner how the tendency of the body to bank inwards (as in the Kolbe curve-bank car) about its high roll-centre RC_2 can be prevented by a location link which holds the body more or less upright and uses the sideways displacement (much exaggerated in the drawing to clarify the illustration) to provide the energy to hold the wheels upright.

The Trebron DRC system would not add much additional weight to a racing car and the use of this no-camber suspension would allow designers to exploit the benefits of the low profile tyre to its fullest extent. Certain critics suggest that the sideways shift of the body could introduce undesirable transient handling problems, but this is most unlikely if the shift is not much greater at one end of the car than at the other. Meanwhile we can only hope that Mr. Hamy finds the money to exploit his intriguing idea. All we can offer is encouragement.

DAMPERS

The dampers on racing and sports cars are invariably of the telescopic type in which oil is displaced through fixed orifices and spring-loaded valves by the movement of a piston inside a telescopic tube (see Fig 3.28). Since the piston displacement

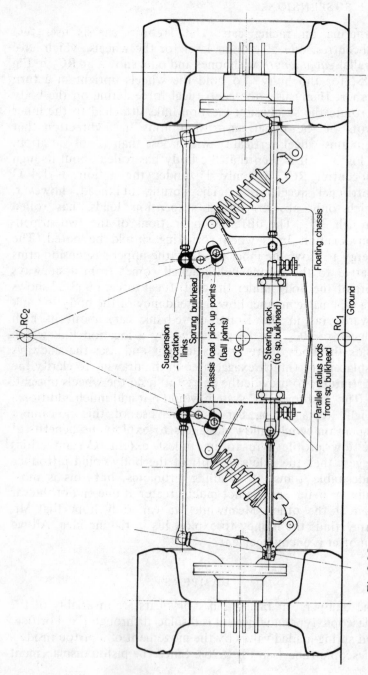

Fig 3.25 Trebron DRC (double roll centre) suspension applied to racing car–static position.

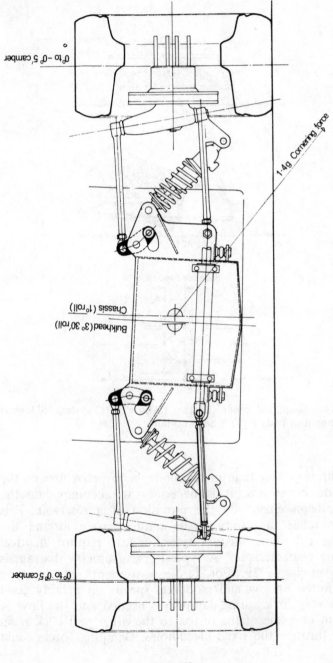

0° to −0° 5' camber

1.4g Cornering force

Chassis (1° roll)

Bulkhead (3° 30' roll)

0° to 0° 5' camber

Fig 3.26 Trebron DRC racing chassis under 1.4 G cornering acceleration. The wheels remain upright as centrifugal force causes the chassis to swing about the upper roll centre.

69

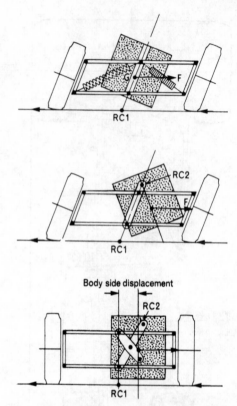

Fig 3.27   Simplified model of the Trebron DRC system. Sideways displacement of body holds wheels upright.

in bump is greater than in rebound, the effective area on the road-side being less, it is necessary to accommodate the excess displacement by the provision of a reservoir. This usually takes the form of an annular space around the working cylinder. No two types of car require identical damping characteristics. A typical force/velocity diagram is shown in Fig 3.29. For gentle movements of the type encountered at low and moderate speeds on a fairly good surface very little spring damping is needed and the flow of oil from one side of the piston to the other and back again occurs through the fixed bleed-holes. Damping forces could

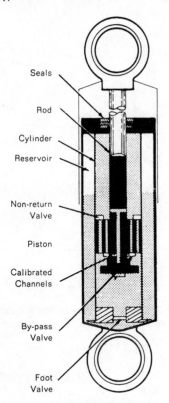

Seals

Rod

Cylinder

Reservoir

Non-return
Valve

Piston

Calibrated
Channels

By-pass
Valve

Foot
Valve

Fig 3.28   Cross-section of a Koni telescopic damper.

not be allowed to increase along curve A, however, since the
damping would be excessive at the higher wheel displace-
ments and at the higher velocities of these wheel movements
that occur when the car is travelling at high speed. To provide
a variable resistance to cope with these higher oil displace-
ments 'ride-control' valves are provided. These are set to open
at a designed pressure and to give a gradually widening
passage for the increased flow of oil as piston velocities
increase. Damping force thus follows curve B in Fig 3.29
under the action of the ride-control valve. In Fig 3.28 the
ride-control valve is called the by-pass valve. The foot-valve is
the valve used to pass the excess fluid into the annular
reservoir.

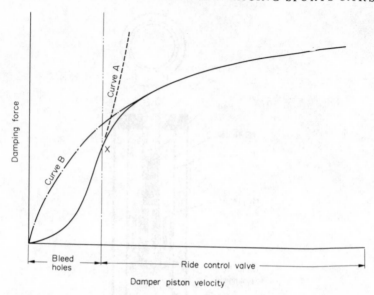

Damper piston velocity

Fig 3.29   Typical damping force/piston velocity curve. X indicates the transition point from control by bleed holes to control by ride control valve.

The choice of damper settings is a matter for compromise. There is, as yet, no perfect damper. Fig 3.30 illustrates the effect of different degrees of damping on the upward accelerations given to the sprung mass over a wide range of wheel oscillation frequencies. f_n is the natural frequency of the suspension; f_r is the frequency at which the wheel is made to oscillate by the ripples in the road surface. Case 1 is that of a completely undamped system and when travelling over a surface with regularly spaced ripples, such as a washboard dirt road), at a speed that causes these forced oscillations to coincide exactly with the natural frequency ($f_r/f_n = 1$) the suspension system will *resonate*. This means in practice that it will move to the full travel permitted by the bump stops. In theory, as indicated by the graph, it could subject the sprung mass to infinite acceleration. The driver would almost certainly lift his foot off the accelerator when subjected to this severe shaking, but as shown by curve (1) he could reduce the vibrations by travelling at a faster speed. With

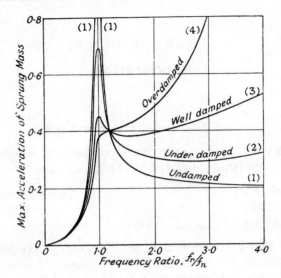

Fig 3.30   Effect of damping on suspension resonance.

poor damping (Case 2) the upward accelerations would still
be severe at resonance, but at higher speeds the accelerations
would drop to an acceptable level (about 0.2 g in the case
shown). Overdamping is seen to control the accelerations at
resonance to as little as 0.4 g, but as the ripple frequency
increases, or the car is driven at a higher speed over the
same series of ripples, the dampers begin to 'harden' and at
very high frequencies, such as traversing a ridge in the road
surface at high speed, the dampers prevent the springs from
moving at all. Case 3 then is a matter for compromise and
will vary from car to car and from circuit to circuit. This is
the reason for the development of adjustable dampers by
such firms as Koni and Armstrong. The latest designs allow
simple adjustments to be made to both the bump and
rebound fittings.

CHAPTER FOUR
Acceleration

ABC OF PEFORMANCE

The limits of performance for a competition sports car or racing car are largely dictated by three factors:

(a) acceleration
(b) braking
(c) cornering

A car that is superior in all three seldom needs the rest of the alphabet. 'S for Speed' is of course of some value, especially on fast circuits like Le Mans and Spa, but sheer speed is not as important as one might think. Stability at speed is more important in a long race.

The Fascination of Acceleration

In drag racing, where acceleration is taken to its current attainable limits, many thousands of fans find the sheer spectacle of so much energy being expended in nothing but noise and smoke and flames, and all to no useful purpose, completely irresistible. Today in America the attendance at official drag strips sanctioned by the National Hot Rod Association exceeds four millions per annum and the number attending unofficial meetings could be almost as great.

Acceleration, up to the legal speed limit, is one of the few legitimate pleasures left to the motorist on the public roads and with a reasonable display of good manners and common sense there is little harm in the activity. The writer is one who believes that motor racing, adequately supervised and with effective spectator protection, is one of the finest ways of sublimating man's aggressive use of the automobile. He therefore has no compunction in encouraging the enjoyment of acceleration in the right place and in the right vehicle. – Or expressed less pompously, it is all good clean fun.

The Limits of Acceleration

Since a car accelerates by applying torque to the driving wheels, which in turn create a forward thrust between the tyre contact patches and the road surface, it is obvious that the limiting grip of the driven tyres on the road surface is one factor that controls the ultimate rate of acceleration. Typical passenger car tyres today are capable of transmitting a force at the contact patch on a good dry surface to give an acceleration of about 1.0 g (where g is equal to the gravitational pull of the earth) Road-racing tyres as used by racing sports cars have a limit of about 1.5 g and the latest 'slicks' used in drag racing are covered with a super-stiction compound that will transmit as much as 1.7 g, but only at the expense of a large amount of this compound. The part played by wheel-spin in transmitting these forces will be discussed later.

The Mechanics of Acceleration

The simple law of motion propounded by Isaac Newton tells us that the rate of acceleration imparted to any body varies directly as the force applied to the body and inversely as its mass, i.e.

$$A = \frac{F}{M} \text{ in any consistent units.}$$

F is the net. force available for acceleration, since some of the thrust applied to the contact patches is absorbed in frictional losses between the road surface and the tyres and some is dissipated in aerodynamic drag.

The engine transmits its torque to the wheels via the clutch and transmission system. Torque is only another way of saying 'twisting action', i.e. a certain force applied to twist a drive shaft at a certain distance and is usually expressed in lb ft. The system of gears incorporated in the gear box and final drive bevel box of the transmission system multiplies this torque by reducing the speed. Typical maximum torque from a 3-litre racing/sports engine would be 250 lb ft. With a final drive ratio of 3.5 to 1 the torque at the drive wheels in top gear would be, approximately:

$$250 \times 3.5 \times 0.97 = 847 \text{ lb ft}$$

We have taken a top gear transmission efficiency of 97 per cent.

In first gear, taking a typical ratio of 2.5 to 1, the available torque at the drive wheels with a transmission loss of 8 per cent would be:

$$250 \times 2.5 \times 3.5 \times 0.92 = 2015 \text{ lb ft}$$

If we take the effective tyre diameter at the convenient figure of 2 ft, the maximum force applied by the drive wheels to the road surface will be 2015 lb in bottom gear and 847 lb in top gear. If we take the loaded car weight at 2500 lb a force of 2015 lb applied to the road surface should give an acceleration in gravities of about 0.8 g in bottom gear. During the early stages of acceleration in top gear, despite a certain loss from air and road resistance, the acceleration would probably still exceed 0.25 g.

We must now confess that we have allowed ourselves to oversimplify in the above calculations. We haved assumed that the torque available at the flywheel is identical to the torque that the engine would provide *when running at a steady speed.* The engine itself, however, must have its rotating parts and reciprocating parts accelerated at the same time as the car is being accelerated. In other words a certain percentage of the power produced by the engine is lost in increasing the rev/min of the engine itself. Not only the engine, but the shafts and gears in the gearbox and the final drive unit and the propellor shaft (when fitted) and the drive shafts and couplings and the wheels and tyres are all accelerating in a rotational sense and power is necessary to produce this acceleration. How much of the steady speed torque is lost in this way depends upon the type of vehicle. For an M Type MG Midget which accelerated from 0 to 50 m.p.h. in about one minute flat, the rotational losses would be negligible, as indeed would be the rate of acceleration! At the other end of the scale are cars like the McLaren Can-Am sports car with a dry weight of 1500 lb and a genuine power available at the flywheel exceeding 70 b.h.p. (this being the power measured by dynamometer at constant engine speed). Such a car will accelerate from 0 to 100 m.p.h. in 6 seconds and to 60 m.p.h. in 4 seconds. During the early stages of such a run about fifty per cent of the power is absorbed in accelerating the engine, gear-box and drive masses over the operating range of each gear. Even though the wheels and tyres on a modern racing sports car have such a high total mass their rotational speed is much lower that that of the engine components, about one third the rev/min in top gear and about an eighth or even less in bottom gear. On a typical competition sports cars of 3 litres with a running weight of 2000 lb about 35 per cent of the effective engine torque will be absorbed in accelerating the engine in bottom gear and only about 6 per cent in rotational acceleration of the four wheels and tyres. In top gear the losses in accelerating the engine will be reduced to about 8 per cent, with as much as 4 per cent still absorbed in wheel rotation.

There is an important lesson to be learned in all this. The use of lightened flywheels, slipper-type pistons, titanium connecting rods, titanium gears and shafts in the transmission system, even to a reduced extent, the use of lightweight wheels, all help to reduce acceleration times in two ways. Directly they reduce the total mass of the car. By Newton's Law the rate of acceleration will be increased in direct proportion to the reduction in weight. As an added bonus, since they reduce the power lost in accelerating the whole power unit and drive train through its speed range in each gear, they increase the effective torque available at the contact patches to produce the acceleration of this lightened vehicle.

Wheel Spin
Even the most mundane of vehicles on the road today can leave black marks on the road surface when started in the appropriate manner in bottom gear. It is common misconception that we lose acceleration in this way, although of course, to the drag racer his major skill is demonstrated by his fine control of wheel spin at take-off. Two factors must be judged to a nicety to achieve the optimum acceleration from a standing start. By spinning the drive wheels the engine can be made to operate on a more favourable part of the torque curve. One could use more clutch slip to build up the engine speed but only to a limited extent. The more powerful the engine the easier it is to burn out the clutch in a

standing start, The second reason for spinning the wheels
is to obtain maximum traction from the tyres. Just as
we need a slip angle to generate cornering force, so we
require wheel spin to obtain a good grip in a forward
direction. The static coefficient of friction exerted by the
tyre in pure rolling motion may be anything from 0.3 to 0.8
on a good dry surface, depending upon the rubber compound
and the tyre pressure. At some optimum value of wheel spin,
expressed in terms of percentage slip, the coefficient of
adhesion (not a true coefficient of friction under wheel spin)
rises to a peak value. The peak is soon passed (see Fig 4.1) and
the need for skilful throttle control to keep the forward
thrust exerted on the road surface as close as possible to the
peak of this curve during several seconds of initial acceleration must be readily seen from the shape of this curve. The
problem hardly arises if the driver has fairly average skill and
the car is a typical family saloon. It is only in the type of
machinery that is our present interest that we meet the
problem of excessive wheelspin, especially when accelerating
out of a slow corner in the wet.

With excessive wheelspin in the dry, which usually happens
on the starting grid, and is a product of nerves and the

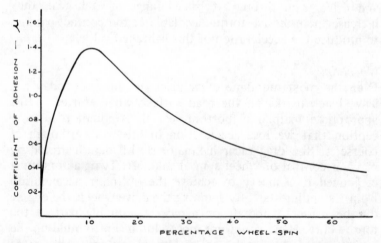

Fig 4.1   Curve of adhesion coefficient versus wheelspin for a typical
tread compound.

difficulty of a driver hearing his own engine, the heat generated at the contact patches is so great that both rubber and asphalt are soon melted. The black streaks left in the road surface can be composed of melted rubber, melted asphalt or a mixture of the two. It all depends upon the relative melting points of the two materials and they both have a wide range. On a concrete surface it is of course always rubber.

THE CHOICE OF DRIVES

This is a question that has arisen so many times in the past and will continue to plague designers of racing cars for years to come. The advantages of FWD in the precarious conditions of poor road adhesion have been adequately demonstrated in European and Trans-Continental Rallies, even in the mud of British Rallycross events, for more than a decade by all types of British Leyland Mini and by those incredible Saabs. There is little doubt in most of our minds that a good design of FWD car will equal the best RWD cars and surpass the majority of them when cornering on slippery roads. Nevertheless we know that the RWD rear-engined vehicle is still supreme on the Grand Prix circuits and in international sports car racing. To understand the reasons for this apparent paradox we must examine the behaviour of the three drive systems under conditions of maximum acceleration. How the three systems behave in a corner will be considered in the next chapter.

In the past FWD has been successfully applied to a few medium-powered racing cars. Even so it is doubtful if the successes of the FWD Millers and Derbys (which were only modified Millers) can in the main be attributed to superior acceleration on cornering. By using FWD the designer got rid of the propellor shaft, so awkwardly placed down the centre of the car. This gave a much lower seating position than in the front-engined RWD racing cars. The cars were lighter and lower and had a smaller frontal area. Inevitably they were faster.

The four wheel drive (4WD) racing car is not new but it received renewed attention about three years ago when the designers of Formula 1 cars became aware of the rising powers of 3-litre engines and concerned about the ability of two relatively small contact patches to transmit the power to the road. While they experimented with 4WD, however, the tyre companies were also experimenting with wider and wider tyres and new rubber compounds. It was the success of the tyre companies efforts rather than the failure of the 4WD prototypes that persuaded the Formula 1 competitors to shelve their plans for further 4WD expenditure.

4WD can be exceptionally stable and well-mannered in a corner, particularly if the chosen torque-split between front and rear wheels is suited to the radius of the corner. During acceleration weight is transferred from front to rear and, to take full advantage of the additional loading on the rear tyres, the designer may chose to transfer 60 per cent of the total torque to the rear and only 40 per cent to the front. For perfect behaviour in a corner however it would be preferable to have a torque split that exactly matched the weight distribution of the car. A small imbalance is not of much consequence and the cornering behaviour of most 4WD racing cars is entirely stable and predictable. One effect of applying 4WD to the new low profile tyres that had not been anticipated by the Formula 1 designers was the fatiguing feed-back of self-aligning torque to the steering wheel when driving torque was applied to the wide front wheels. The tyres on the front FWD Millers were only 4 inches wide and round in profile too! Drivers of these Formula 1 prototypes were so enervated towards the end of a race by the effort involved during cornering that the torque applied to the front wheels was reduced to 30 per cent and towards the end of the season to as little as 20 per cent of the total by some of the team managers. Since the 4WD cars were heavier than the normal RWD cars and gained very little in acceleration or cornering with such a reduced torque-split it is not surprising that they were not competitive. Power steering does at first appear to be a simple answer to the problem, but the majority of racing drivers object to the dead unresponsive feel of power steering. Without a certain amount of 'feed-back' from the camber forces exerted at the tyre contacts the driver would not be able to feel how close he was to the limit of adhesion. There must, of course, be an answer to this problem and it will no doubt be solved when 4WD is eventually seen as the only system that can win in the end.

No designer in recent years has thought of making an FWD racing car and the reasons become more apparent when we consider what happens to the instantaneous loads on the front and rear wheels when a racing sports car is accelerating hard in a straight line. The RWD car of identical power to weight ratio will always out-accelerate the FWD car so long as the grip of the tyres on the road is better than about 0.7μ, where μ is the coefficient of road adhesion. Modern racing tyres on a good dry surface will give coefficients of 1.2 to 1.4, depending upon the particular rubber compound.

Fig. 4.2 shows how the rear tyres become more heavily loaded and the front more lightly loaded during hard acceleration. Since the centre of gravity of the sprung mass is at height, h, above the road surface a couple is set up during acceleration which is equal to this distance times the tractive forces at the contact patches of the driving wheels. In the figure this tractive force is represented by F_1 for a rear drive car or by F_2 for a front drive car. This couple increases the loads on the rear springs and decreases those at the front.

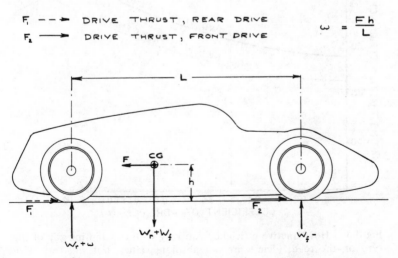

Fig 4.2   Dynamic wheel loads during acceleration.

Under very high rates of acceleration, as for example we see on a dragster, this couple can make the front wheels lift clear of the ground, which no doubt explains why we never see FWD dragsters.

The limiting tractive effort that a car can transmit to the road is:—

$$F_{max} = (W_f - w)\mu \text{ for an FWD car}$$
$$= (W_r + w)\mu \text{ for an RWD car}$$
$$= (W_f + W_r)\mu \text{ for a 4WD car}$$

where $W_f - w$ is the dynamic load on the front wheels $W_r + w$ is the dynamic load of the rear wheels and μ is the limiting coefficient of adhesion between the tyres and the road.

A 4WD car can be considered to achieve a tractive efficiency of 100 per cent when the torque-split between

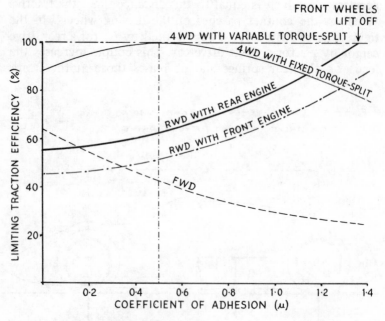

Fig 4.3   How tractive efficiency can vary with the limiting grip of the tyre on the road. (These are not absolute values, but will vary with wheelbase, weight distribution and height of CG).

front and rear wheels is exactly equal to the instantaneous ratio of the dynamic loads on the front and rear wheels and when no differential torque occurs from side to side. The first condition will only occur at one particular rate of acceleration and the second will only occur with a locked differential in the early stages of a standing start run. In practice the designer must compromise by choosing a torque-split to give maximum efficiency at some point in the range. In Fig 4.3 the designed maximum tractive efficiency point has been chosen for a value of $\mu = 0.5$.

One cannot generalize when applying the above formulae to different types of road vehicle. The extent of the load transfer from front to rear varies with the ratio h/L. For a vehicle such as a Jeep the amount of load transfer for a given rate of acceleration will be about 3 times as high as it would be on a Formula 1 car. The graphs of Fig 4.3 therefore are only given to illustrate a principle and will be changed in slope if the CG of the sprung mass is raised or lowered, the wheelbase is changed or the front/rear weight distributions are changed. For the graphs of Fig 4.3 the following static weight distributions have been taken as typical for good designs of racing sports car:—

(a) 65/35 weight distribution for an FWD car
(b) 55/45 weight distribution for a front-engined RWD car
(c) 45/55 weight distribution for a rear-engined RWD car
(d) 47/53 weight distribution for a 4WD car

When we consider the implications of these curves the following facts emerge:

1. for the whole range of possible road conditions, from ice and mud (or oil-slicked asphalt) to hard dry asphalt or concrete, 4WD will give the highest rate of acceleration (where sufficient power is available to make tractive efficiency the limiting factor).

2. The advantage of 4WD begins to disappear as coefficients of adhesion of 1.0 are reached and with sufficient power available and tyre adhesions exceeding 1.2 the advantage could well be lost to the rear-engined RWD car,

particularly when this car is appreciably lighter in construction.

3. Next to the 4WD car the FWD car is the most accelerative in ice, snow and mud (μ = 0.05 to 0.20). This explains the frequent successes of such vehicles in Winter Rallies.

4. The front-engined RWD car is severely handicapped by its forward weight bias and has little to recommend it for competitive motoring.

CHAPTER FIVE
Cornering

Cornering is the very essence of motor racing. Several books have been written on the techniques used by racing drivers and a large proportion of such books is usually devoted to the techniques used when cornering: the correct line to take with an understeering car, with an oversteering car, control of direction by means of the throttle, the Nuvolari technique, the Moss technique, etc, etc. They seldom bother to tell you what to do on the straights! Our concern is the car, not the driver, and the part played by the car when cornering near the limit is no less important than the ability to handle the car.

THE BALANCE OF FORCES IN A CONSTANT RADIUS CURVE

By definition acceleration is *change of velocity*. Velocity has two dimensions, magnitude and direction. The layman's concept of acceleration is one of change in the magnitude of a velocity, i.e. a car going faster in a straight line, or slowing down when braking, which is deceleration. Acceleration also occurs when a body changes direction, even though the speed does not change. A train that goes round a curve in the track or a car that turns a corner must be accelerated if the speed relative to the rails or the road surface is to remain unchanged. The cornering force, or centrifugal force as we call it, to create this centrifugal acceleration is applied, in the case of a car, at the four contact patches.

Fig 5.1 shows how the forces acting on the four tyres at road level balance the centrifugal force acting at the centre of gravity of the car's mass. The car in this case is a conventional front engine/rear drive vehicle. Since torque to maintain the acceleration (i.e. to keep the car running at constant speed throughout the bend) is applied to the rear contact patches, the resultant forces, R_0 on the outer wheel and R_i on the

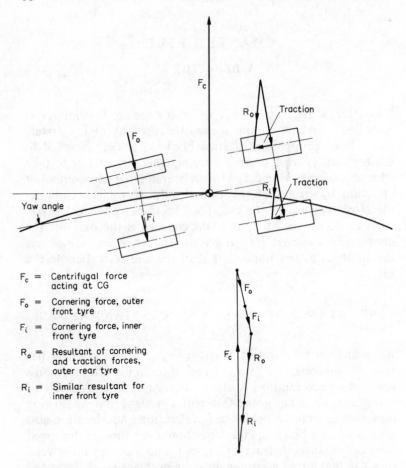

F_c = Centrifugal force
        acting at CG

F_o = Cornering force, outer
        front tyre

F_i = Cornering force, inner
        front tyre

R_o = Resultant of cornering
        and traction forces,
        outer rear tyre

R_i = Similar resultant for
        inner front tyre

Fig 5.1   RWD with front engine. Balance of forces when cornering.

inner wheel are not at right-angles to the plane of the wheels,
but are angled forwards depending upon the relative dimensions of the drive thrust and the pure radial cornering force.
The centrifugal force at the C.G. and the resisting forces at
the contact patches are in different planes. This causes the
body to roll as shown in Fig 5.2. Roll places greater loads on
the outer tyres and this in turn means that the outer tyres
transmit a greater proportion of the force to resist the
centrifugal force than the inner tyre.

ROLL INCREASES DYNAMIC LOAD
ON OUTER TYRES WITH A
CORRESPONDING DECREASE ON INNER

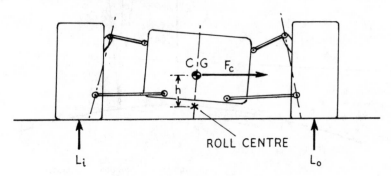

Fig 5.2   Load transfer due to roll.

In the example of Fig 5.1 the C.G. is equidistant from the axes of the front and rear wheels. In a rear-engined car one would expect a more tail-heavy weight distribution and the rear tyres would have to provide a greater percentage of the total resisting force. With a front heavy car, such as a Mini-Cooper, the major forces are provided by the front tyres. Fig 5.3 shows the balance of forces for a rear-engined car. For simplicity the inner and outer wheels are combined into a single unit at each end of the car. Fig 5.4 shows a similar simplified force diagram for an FWD car and Fig 5.5 applies to a 4WD car.

Since the cornering forces that can be exerted by the contact patches are in all four cases dependent upon the limiting factors of threshold slip angles (the slip angle where a large increase in angle gives no increase in cornering force) and the prevailing road adhesion coefficient a study of the four force diagrams shows that the fastest car through a bend of constant radius is one where the front and rear tyre forces (considering resultant forces) are perfectly parallel. The more open the triangle of forces the slower will the car be through the bend when driven at the limit. Surprisingly, the rear-engined car which is so popular today in single-seater racing form and in racing sports cars provides a fairly open triangle

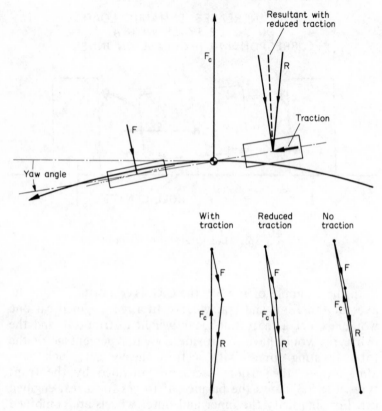

Fig 5.3   RWD with rear engine. Simplified cornering force diagrams.

of forces, being more open when 'accelerating' through the bend, i.e. with a considerable tractive effort applied to the driven wheels.

In one particular case of the FWD car the amount of forward thrust required to give the required propulsion to maintain a steady speed through the bend brings the resultant force exactly in parallel with the rear tyre forces. This is entirely fortuitous. With a greater or less acceleration the lines of force would not be exactly parallel. Nevertheless the inherent advantage of front wheel drive over rear wheel drive is well demonstrated.

When we consider four wheel drive we see that the

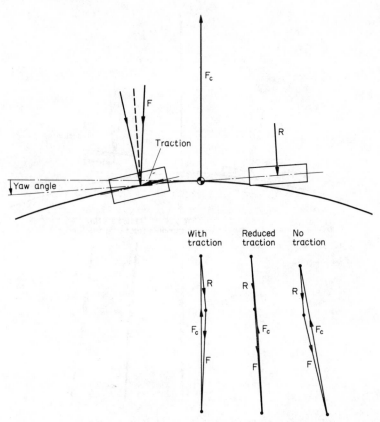

Fig 5.4   FWD, simplified cornering force diagrams.

optimum cornering forces depends upon the manner in which
the total drive torque is apportioned between the two ends of
the car. For a tight bend more torque will be required at the
front to achieve parallel resultant forces, for a large radius
high-speed bend a larger percentage at the rear. The use of a
fixed torque-split is a reasonable compromise and has been
shown on racing cars like the Felday Four, which uses the
Ferguson 4WD system to give very stable handling when
accelerating, braking and cornering under a wide range of
running conditions.

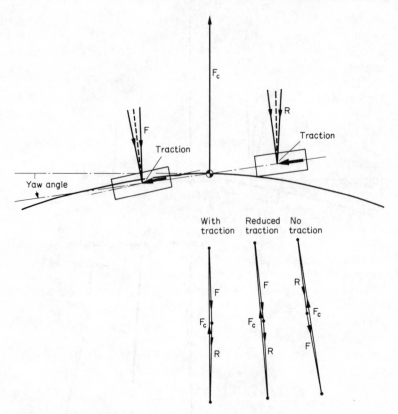

Fig 5.5   4WD, simplified cornering force diagrams.

Stability in a Corner

The ability of an FWD car to out-perform an RWD car on almost any shape or radius of corner is not likely to be disputed, yet we find that the RWD transmission is the one chosen almost universally in racing today. To understand why this is so we must consider the behaviour of the two drive systems when cornering near the limit. Consider first the case of an FWD car cornering at the limit of tyre adhesion with just enough torque applied to the front wheels to bring the resultant tyre forces at the front precisely into line with the centrifugal force (as in Fig 5.4). If under any circumstances the driver finds it necessary to lift his foot off the accelerator he is liable to be in trouble. If we study the implications of Figs 2.7 and 2.8b in Chapter Two we see that a reduction in traction will immediately reduce the front slip angles, since the radial component, f_c is no longer running at the limit of adhesion (the radius of the circle of forces, F_c). Unfortunately for the driver any change which reduces the front slip angles relative to the rear results in a tightening of the turning circle which in turn increases the magnitude of the centrifugal force. The rear tyres however are already operating at the limiting slip angles for the original centrifugal force. Consequently the rear end breaks away and the car, unless driven by a genius, goes into a spin. A clever designer can reduce this tendency by designing a high degree of roll-steer into the car. With about two-thirds of the total mass concentrated at the front, as in the case of the Cooper S, the increased roll induced by the increased centrifugal force can be made to give a roll-steer effect which is greater at the front than the rear. This then is an understeering effect which will tend to reduce the turning circle. Unfortunately there is always a lag in the action of roll-steer and the spin can have taken place before the roll-steer has had much effect on the path of the car. We can therefore say, in all fairness, that the FWD car which is perfectly safe at the cornering speeds used by normal road users can be placed in a situation of 'no return' when a racing driver uses traction to reach the ultimate in cornering power. If he is baulked slightly by another competitor, or finds he has entered the bend 2 or 3 m.p.h. higher than his usual limit, there is no escape since he dare not back off on the throttle.

When the driver of an RWD racing car finds himself in a similar situation and eases his foot, or lifts it completely from the accelerator the effect is to reduce the slip angles at the rear. This is an understeering action and tends to reduce the centrifugal force. Moreover, as will be seen from Fig 5.3, the front and rear tyre resultant forces come more into line, thus increasing their combined cornering power so that the car will run at lower slip angles at both front and rear as soon as the accelerator is eased. Under these conditions the driver is given some leeway to choose a modified line through the corner, even steering to pass a slower competitor. We now see why rear-engined RWD racing and racing sports cars have been so successful. With a weight biased towards the rear and larger rear tyres to compensate for this bias the influence of traction in a corner is almost as great as the steering wheel especially on a Formula 1 car with more than 450 b.h.p. available and a running weight of about 1600 lb. The driver literally steers with his right foot. The yaw angle, the angle between the car's centre-line and the direction in which the CG is travelling, as shown in Fig 5.3 can be increased or reduced by applying more or less traction to the rear wheels. Since these rear tyres are larger and more heavily loaded than the front they transmit the major part of the cornering force and the driver finds he has excellent control over the car from entering to leaving the bend.

Where then is the need for 4WD? The advantages of driving all four wheels has been shown to be marginal in the previous chapter, but there is still a gain to be made in cornering since the triangle of forces when traction is applied in a corner is much closer to the ideal case of parallel front and rear tyre thrusts (the ideal case shown in Fig 5.4 for an FWD car). Moreover with no traction the increased limiting forces in a radial direction that automatically occurs when traction forces or braking forces are removed (see 'circle of forces', Fig 2.7) occurs simultaneously *at both ends*. Apart from a change in the angle of yaw, easily corrected at the steering wheel, the driver hardly notices any change in the handling behaviour of the car, with or without traction in a corner and this sense of stability is surely of some value.

Swerve Response

A manoeuvre that is the equivalent of the slalom in skiing is the S-turn in motor racing. Sometimes the manoeuvre is demanded by an artificial chicane, sometimes the act of passing another competitor immediately followed by lining up the car for the next bend involves a quick left-right or right-left swerve, all done at near-limiting tyre adhesion forces. It is the ability to make rapid changes in direction that separates the cowboy's quarter-horse from the cart-horse, the corvette from the battleship, the sports car from the limousine. It was Maurice Olley of General Motors who first drew our attention to the influence of the polar moment of inertia of a car. A car with a high polar moment of inertia will have less tendency to pitch on ripples in a motorway surface. Unfortunately this high inertia also makes it less manoeuvrable when darting from lane to lane in traffic.

The Dumb-bell Effect

The entire mass of a car is made up of thousands of separate components, some light, such as body panels, some heavy such as engines and fuel tanks. The concept of a centre of gravity is easy to understand, being the centre at which the sum of the individual smaller masses that make up the whole may be considered to be concentrated when the action of gravity or other accelerations are being applied to the whole body. When we are considering the inertia of a body subjected to a rapid rotation, or even an angular deflection about its C.G., the disposition of these masses about the C.G. becomes important. If we consider a mass of 10 lb situated at a distance of 1 ft from the C.G., the act of swinging this mass about the C.G. through a certain angle in a given unit of time will require X lbf. Another component of the car also weighing 10 lb, but at a distance of 4 ft from the C.G. would require a force of 16X lbf to move it through the same angle in the same time. Not only is its leverage about the C.G. greater, but it has a greater distance to move in the same unit of time and the combined effect is to make its resistance to movement in a circular path, what we call *the polar moment of inertia*, vary as *the square* of the distance from the C.G. From this we can move on to the concept of a radius of gyration, which is the radius at which the mass of the car may be considered to be concentrated, relative to C.G. (equally distributed in a thin line at radius K, or as two dumb-bell weights at radius K as shown in 5.6) and to have the identical polar moment of inertia as that of the actual car.

A large sedan or limousine as shown in Fig 5.6a obviously has a high polar moment of inertia; the dumb-bell effect is high. With the help of power steering the driver can try to execute a very rapid S-turn, but the forces involved in making this large dumb-bell first swing in one direction and then the

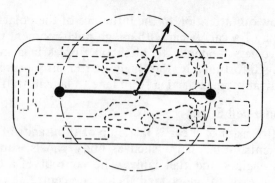

(a) HIGH POLAR MOMENT OF INERTIA

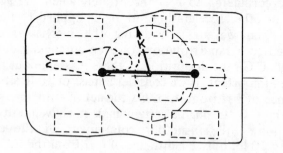

(b) LOW POLAR MOMENT OF INERTIA

Fig 5.6   Distribution of major masses influences the radius of gyration, K.

other demands such high forces from the tyre contact patches that the car will not necessarily follow the path requested by the driver. If the limiting adhesion coefficient for the particular road conditions is exceeded the car will simply slide in a straight line. It is important to remember that the entire mass of the car is involved in the problem of reducing this polar moment of inertia. The wheels and tyres and suspension components are all involved in angular movements in a horizontal plane. The secondary effect of a slalom turn which we discussed in Chapter Three when defining *roll-steer* and later under the heading 'Slalom Turns' is that the roll of the body on its suspension system lags behind the steering input. This body roll, depending upon the disposition of the main masses of the body/frame structure along the longitudinal centre-line and upon the stiffness of the springs, can provoke an understeering or an oversteering tendency which lags behind the initial steering response. If we reduce the polar moment of inertia of the *sprung mass*, therefore, we help to improve the S-turn behaviour in two ways, since the total polar moment is reduced and the roll-steer effects are also reduced.

This then is the reason for concentrating the main components, the greater masses, as near as possible to the C.G. of a racing car. Side-mounted radiators instead of front-mounted radiators; mid-engine location instead of rear or front; a tranaxle with the gearbox ahead of the rear wheels instead of behind; fuel tanks in the mid-section instead of the front or rear; light alloy components wherever practical; all these are conscious efforts made by the designer of a racing car to keep the polar moment of inertia as low as is humanly possible. Since designers are but human some are more successful in achieving this than others.

CHAPTER SIX

Braking

It has been said that the great Nuvolari seldom used his brakes, relying almost entirely on the use of the gearbox to lose speed as he entered a corner. He would sometimes put the car into an alarming slide to scrub off speed, yet he retained sufficient control to enter the corner at the correct angle of yaw and at the correct speed. Reports from mechanics who accompanied him confirm that he seldom used the brakes. It also confirms that Nuvolari knew only too well how unreliable were the brakes on all types of racing cars in the era in which he raced. Even with the well-cooled large diameter brakes used on such classic racing cars as the Alfa Romeo P2 and P3 and the MG Magnette K3 Nuvolari knew by experience that excessive use of the brakes in the early stages of a race could lead to disastrous failure when required to avoid a collision in the final stages. Today we call this sudden loss of braking effort when linings and drums become overheated 'brake-fade'. The words used by Nuvolari's contemporaries to describe it cannot be repeated here!

The modern racing driver takes his brakes for granted. He relies upon consistent performance at the same section of a circuit, lap after lap, and with rare exceptions he gets it. Braking up to the limits of tyre adhesion is normal. No modern Nuvolari is likely to appear on the scene who can substitute sheer driving virtuosity for the power of modern brakes.

DISC BRAKES

For the braking of high performance cars today one need only consider the design of the disc brake. First used by Lanchester in 1906 it was considered to be a poor alternative to the drum brake at the time. The mud and dust thrown at it as the car travelled over the unsurfaced roads of the period often rendered it ineffective when most needed. More than forty years elapsed before the Dunlop Rubber Company began to experiment with a modified version of their aircraft disc brake on sports cars. In 1953 a convincing demonstration of the superiority of disc brakes was given when a C Type Jaguar fitted with Dunlop disc brakes won the 24 hours of Le Mans at an average speed of nearly 106 m.p.h. The Jaguar drivers were reported to be delaying the start of braking at the end of the Mulsanne Straight to a point 300 yards closer to the corner than their drum-braked rivals.

The advantages of disc brakes are summarized below:—

1. increased resistance to fade.
2. stability of braking force; no large changes in the coefficient of friction.
3. excellent water recovery compared with drum brakes.
4. improved directional stability.

The disadvantages are:—

1. a higher rate of pad wear in comparison with drum linings (the inboard pads, being subjected to a higher rate of wear than the outboard, since they are sprayed with more grit and mud from the road surface).
2. brake squeal is more prevalent in disc brakes, but this is purely a problem for the production car designer.
3. discs are more prone to suffer scoring of the pad contact surface than drum brakes, especially in dirty wet conditions.

For nearly twenty years disc brakes have been the complete answer to the catastrophic type of brake fade we used to experience with drum brakes under racing conditions. Nevertheless the increase in the maximum speeds of racing sports cars from about 150 m.p.h. in 1953 to as much as 240 m.p.h. in 1972 has more than doubled the power to be dissipated in heat when braking at the end of a long straight. If brake applications of this magnitude are followed in fairly rapid succession by other less severe applications around the rest of the circuit it is possible for the pad material to reach temperatures never reached during practice, temperatures of 800°C or even 900°C (1470–1650°F).

When the temperatures of the pads reach a new high it is

not uncommon for more resin to decompose. When this depolymerized resin (a constituent used during manufacture to bind the friction materials) leeches out it lubricates the surface temporarily, giving a small reduction in braking effort. The effect is not great, usually only resulting in a loss of about ten per cent of the normal braking force. It is in any case advisable to keep pad temperatures below 700°C (1295°F) since pad wear increases rapidly at higher temperatures. A wise driver today attempts to minimize wear so that less time is lost at the pits while new pads are fitted.

Zora Arkus-Duntov, who has been in charge of development of the Chevrolet Corvette since its inception in the early Fifties, decided in 1964 that his 3000 lb 150 m.p.h. sports car could no longer be stopped in a safe consistent manner by means of drum brakes. From extensive experiments carried out on normal (solid) and ventilated (hollow and fitted with internal radial vanes to produce air flow) disc brakes he found that the Delco Moraine ventilated disc brake had a 78 per cent greater heat dissipating capacity than a normal disc brake of the same diameter. It is therefore not surprising that the designers of Grand Prix and racing sports cars have all since adopted ventilated disc brakes. Improvements in tyre compounds have encouraged the safe use of greater rates of deceleration (as much as 1.0 g at speeds below 100 m.p.h.) and this has now exceeded the heat dissipating capacity of solid discs. The use of aerofoils and wedge profile bodies has also added to the problem.

The disc is, of course, only half the picture in the saga of the disc brake. The material that rubs against the disc and its ability to maintain an almost constant coefficient of friction at temperatures up to 900°C (1650°F) can sometimes be the deciding factor in a race. The Ferodo Company started life in the last century making fibre blocks to rub against the iron rims of cart wheels. 'Much superior to old rope, leather, etc.' claims an early Ferodo advertisement and they would no doubt claim even more for their famous DS11 pad material which has been used by almost every racing team in Europe over the last few years. The attraction of DS11 has been its consistent performance, since the coefficient of friction stays almost constant at 0.30 from 0°C (32°F) with an imperceptible rise to 0.31 at 900°C (1650°F). DS11 has a random fibre asbestos base and an evenly dispersed inclusion of copper particles. Bedding-in of new pads is achieved by making two or three slowish laps with frequent, but gentle, brake applications. During this period the pads develop a glaze which is caused by the copper particles on the surface melting and forming a thin skin over both the pads and the discs. Since copper melts at 1080°C (1975°F) it is apparent from this that the rubbing surfaces of the particles of copper must exceed this temperature momentarily during the brake applications. During final practice it is advisable for the driver to use his brakes much more heavily. This is called 'pre-fading' the brakes. When fully bedded-in and pre-faded the DS11 material will give a consistent coefficient of 0.30, but when first used at the maximum operating temperature there will be a temporary drop to about 0.25. One cannot risk this happening at a critical stage in the race. Hence the need for the pre-fade technique in the final laps of practice.

STABILITY DURING BRAKING

Hard braking on a good dry surface presents no problems to the experienced driver if his braking system is well designed and well maintained. Panic stops on 11 sports cars, as reported in 'Road & Track' Road Test Annual for 1971, gave mean deceleration rates from 80m.p.h. varying from 0.74 g for the 454 Corvette to 0.93 g for the Ferrari 365 GTB/4. The Ferrari stopping distance was 270 ft, the Corvette 310 ft. With racing tyres decelerations of at least 1.0 g would have been achieved by the Ferrari.

On slippery road surfaces the experienced driver uses the brakes with the knowledge that locked wheels do not give optimum retardation. Fig 6.1 serves to show how critical this can be. These graphs only serve to illustrate the behaviour of the contact patch under braking, which, not surprisingly is very similar to the behaviour under acceleration. The values shown in Fig 6.1 only relate to one particular set of tyre compound/road surface combinations. If we changed to a softer compound the curves would be of very different shape.

Locked front wheels will not steer and the good driver,

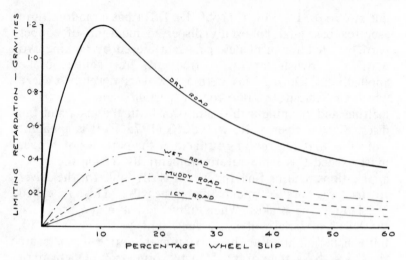

Fig 6.1   Graphs of limiting retardation versus wheel spin.

being well aware of this, tries to maintain some directional control on a slippery surface by applying the brakes in a series of quick short jabs, so that the wheels are never sliding for more than a fraction of a second. On these grounds it would seem advisable to provide larger brakes at the rear of the car so that these will lock first and allow the front wheels free for steering out of trouble. Unfortunately a car with locked rear wheels only is more liable to spin. Fig 6.2 should help to explain why this is so.

When the rear wheels lock first, as shown in the first diagram, the rear tyres can no longer exert side forces of appreciable magnitude to the road surface. Hence any disturbing force, such as an asymmetric weight distribution (no passenger, for example) or an uneven road surface, will allow this off-centre force (indicated as a small mass, m, displaced distance, x, from the centre-line in the diagram) to pivot ᵗbout the front wheels, where the contact patches are still ᵗapable of exerting side forces. In the second diagram it is the ᵗront wheels that are locked and the rear wheels that are still able to generate side forces. In this case the off-centre mass is ahead of the stabilising grip of the rear tyres and the worst that the off-centre mass, or other disturbing impulse, is likely

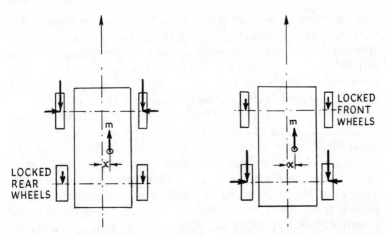

Fig 6.2   Forces disturbing stability when wheels lock: (a) with rear wheels locked, (b) with front wheels locked.

to achieve is a tendency for the car to travel at a small yaw angle.

For safe braking then we have decided that the designer must provide a larger brake pad area on the front discs than on the rear — but how much more? In Table 6.1 the effect of weight transfer on the dynamic wheel loads has been calculated for a range of limiting tyre adhesion coefficients

TABLE 6.1

Retardation rate in gravities	Dynamic wheel loads as % of total wt.		Effect on car
	F	R	
0.05	56	44	Front wheels locked
0.1	56.5	43.5	Front wheels locked
0.2	58.5	41.5	Front wheels locked
0.4	61.5	38.5	Front wheels locked
0.6	65	35	All wheels locked
0.8	68	32	Rear wheels locked
1.0	72	28	Rear wheels locked

from a value as low as 0.05 (smooth ice) to as high as 1.0 (smooth dry asphalt). The calculations are based on a front-engined sports car with a static weight distribution of 55F/45R. The wheelbase is taken as 8 ft, the C.G. is taken as at a height of 16 inches above the road surface and the designed split of braking areas is taken as 65F/35R.

The danger of rear wheel locking is demonstrated to be very real with the chosen ratio of braking areas. A 75/25 ratio is demanded if we are to eliminate this possibility, but the provision of a front pad area that is three times as great as that on the rear wheels seems a high price to have to pay. Today, in the opinion of the author, it is the driver who is paying the penalty, since the orthodox braking systems are demonstrably out-dated and it is only the skill of the driver, in the manner of a tightrope walker who has dropped his pole, that keeps the car pointing in the right direction when they are braking at the limit. There is a solution to this delicate design problem and we will no doubt see one or other of the available anti-lock systems adopted for racing cars in the near future. But before we move on to these solutions let us consider another very real danger that the driver has to face when braking a car from high speed.

Single Wheel Locking

In the above analysis we have only considered front to rear stability as affected by pairs of wheels locking in unision, but we all know that a single wheel will often lock and in certain cases, as when the inner wheels run over a wet patch in the road and the outer wheels are on dry asphalt, it is possible to have both wheels on one side of the road almost unbraked while the other side is under as much as 1.0 g deceleration. There is very little the driver can do in such extreme conditions to prevent the car from turning broadside or spinning. If a high performance car can snake badly when accelerating on a surface with large variations in adhesion one can hardly expect the driver to hold it on a straight course in the more unstable conditions of braking.

Anti-lock Braking

Brake manufacturers have been devoting much time in recent years to the development of sensing devices that will prevent wheel-locking. A relatively simple device to prevent locking of the two rear wheels, but not single wheel locking is the Lockheed pressure limiting device, as used on British Leyland Minis. It contains a g-sensitive ball valve, the ball rolling up a ramp to cut off the fluid pressure to the rear brakes at a chosen value of g. This an effective cure for spinning on slippery surfaces, but the car still only has the capability, under the guidance of a typical driver, of travelling in a straight line in conditions of poor adhesion. This is of little value when a stone wall lies straight ahead. Admittedly the top rally drivers can often cope with this sort of situation by such tricks as a controlled application of the hand-brake to momentarily lock the rear wheels and provoke a spin or start the car turning in the direction they require by slalom techniques, but this is really a case of skill triumphing over poor design and the number of rally cars we see wrapped around trees is proof enough that it does not always work.

Dunlop first developed their anti-skid device for aircraft brakes and they began to apply it to car braking about ten years ago. The Maxaret system employs a small flywheel which is driven at the speed of the wheel which it controls. Any small difference in speed, as will happen when a wheel begins to lock is sensed by the Maxaret unit which then permits a partial release of the hydraulic pressure to this wheel. An excellent example of this system is seen on the Ferguson 4WD Prototype car, which must surely be one of the safest cars ever to appear on the road. The original Maxaret units required a high-pressure hydraulic system for their operation. In conjunction with Dunlop the Ferguson Company evolved a method of controlling a standard automobile braking system through the servo units. The Maxaret unit in this case is driven from the central 'Duolok' control system which is part of the balanced system of 4WD developed by Ferguson Research Ltd. and which is fully described in Chapter 11. In this modified Maxaret system the Maxaret unit senses that all four wheels are locked, or that two diagonal wheels are locked, or that two wheels on the same side are locked. No provision is made to cope with single wheel locking in this application. When the Maxaret unit senses wheel locking it sends an electrical signal to a solenoid which controls a shuttle valve. The shuttle valve under the appropriate impulse re-routes the vacuum to the servo from one side of the diaphragm to the other, so that the servo is then working against the driver instead of assisting his effort. In this way the brakes are partially released on the appropriate wheels. In practice the braking forces are eased sufficiently to prevent the particular wheels from reaching the locking point. When driving this R5 prototype the rapid fluttering of the solenoid valve and servo diaphragm can be felt by the driver at the brake pedal when making a panic stop on a wet road surface. The system becomes more effective as speeds increase and surface conditions deteriorate and this is surely the very conditions when racing cars become dangerous. A Maxaret anti-lock system would add about 40 lb to the weight of a racing sports car, but the chances of finishing at Le Mans in the wet would be more than doubled.

More recent anti-lock devices are the WSP system, developed jointly by Lucas and Girling in Great Britain, and the Bosch system from Germany. In the WSP (Wheel Slide Protection) system each wheel is fitted with an inductive sensor which transmits an AC signal proportional to wheel speed. This signal is differentiated to give an analogue of wheel deceleration, or in non-computer language let us say that it can measure the rate of deceleration by means of a magic electronic box. When this rate of deceleration exceeds a chosen reference value, such as 1.3 g, a solenoid is energised which releases the brakes on the particular wheel. An electrically driven hydraulic pump is provided to supply hydraulic fluid at 3000 lb/in^2 to re-activate the brakes as soon as the wheel is freely rotating again. Re-cycling of the brake pressure to the locked wheel is extremely rapid. The WSP controls can re-cycle at least ten times per second and when operating to prevent wheel locking the brake pressure in the rest of the hydraulic circuit will vary by no more than plus or minus 10 per cent.

No racing car designer is likely to adopt an anti-locking system that is not intrinsically 'fail-safe'. To this end the new Bosch and Girling-Lucas systems have been designed so that the normal braking is unaffected by failure of an electronic component or by failure of the anti-locking system's own high-pressure hydraulic system.

CHAPTER SEVEN
Aerodynamics

Pioneers

'Why did I not think of that?' — we usually say when we first see a Hovercraft, or Snowmobile, or even a ring-opening beer can. And then we say — 'having invented these gadgets why do they take so long to develop them?' Look at aerodynamics, for example. Not exactly an invention, but the practical applications of the science of aerodynamics have been with us since those two bright bicycle mechanics succeeded in getting their unstable flying machine into the air about two-thirds of a century ago. With all this long experience behind us it would not be unreasonable to expect us to have learned by now almost everything that could be learned about the aerodynamics of the automobile in motion. The wild experiments with aerofoils on racing cars that started only about five years ago, and are still going on , will serve to show that there is still much to be learned in the application of aerodynamics to racing cars.

Ettore Bugatti was one of the first to realize that the actual size of a racing car, in particular the frontal area, influenced the amount of power wasted in dragging it through the air. He was not only a pioneer in lightweight construction; he was also a pioneer in miniaturization. Anyone who has travelled in one of his earlier racing or sports cars will know exactly how small they were.

The author has a special affection for the Brescia Bugatti, since his first sports car was a 1922 Type 22 Brescia Modifié. In standard form, with two-seater bodywork and a 1.5-litre engine producing little more than 30 b.h.p., this car had a genuine top speed of 75 m.p.h. a remarkable achievement for a car of this era. The racing version was claimed to have a top speed of 100 m.p.h., but with only about 55 b.h.p. available this is almost certainly an exaggerated claim. It is significant, nevertheless, that Bugatti could design a small-engined two-seater sports car to reach a speed of 75 m.p.h. in 1921 when few sports cars of under 2-litres capacity could reach this figure a decade later. The secret of the Bugatti's success was its low frontal area (i.e. the maximum cross-sectional area in front elevation). If we include the projecting portions of the driver and passenger, who were well in the airstream from above chest height, the frontal area of the Type 22 can be taken at a realistic value of about 9 ft². For comparison the frontal area of an MGB GT is 16.4 ft² and some of my well-fed American friends complain that this car is rather tight around the hips. How tight the Type 22 was can be seen from its external body width of 2 ft 3½ in against the 5 ft of the MGB.

BERNOULLI'S LAW

Aerodynamics is a much older science than one might suppose. About 200 years ago the Italian scientist, Daniel Bernoulli, made a very important discovery. His experiments showed that the pressure and velocity of a moving stream of gas or liquid are interchangeable forms of the same energy. When the pressure increases, the velocity falls, and vice versa.
    Bernoulli's Law states:

$$p + \tfrac{1}{2}\rho\ V^2 = \text{Constant}$$

where p is the local pressure
       V is the local velocity
       ρ is the fluid density.

$\tfrac{1}{2}\rho\ V^2$ is called the kinetic energy of the fluid, i.e. the energy associated with its movement.
    In applying Bernoulli's law to the airflow around a car body we usually neglect frictional losses and the effects of gravity. Now that the land speed record has reached 630 m.p.h. it is possible that compressibility effects will have to be considered by such specialist body designers in the near future. At the more modest speeds of racing sports cars we can forget such effects.
    A practical example of Bernoulli's Law is seen in our use of a venturi in the carburettor where the air stream is accelerated by forming a restriction in the passage. As the air velocity is increased the pressure falls below atmospheric,

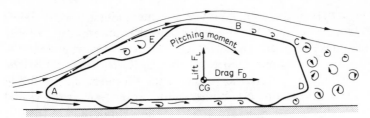

Fig 7.1   Air flow over typical GT body.

thus inducing a fuel flow from the float bowl via the jets. The typical profile of a modern car body, as shown in Fig 7.1, causes an acceleration of the airstream over the upper surface and a corresponding reduction in the local pressure. Maximum pressure (see Fig 7.2) occurs at some point such as A where the air velocity is at its lowest, with another relatively stagnant zone of high pressure created by the windscreen. The maximum depression point B will depend upon the shape of the roof and the magnitude of the depression surviving in the wake (behind D in the figure) depends upon many factors which will be discussed later.

On a typical racing sports car with a low ground clearance drag is created by the interaction of the moving underbody of the car on the layer of air that lies between it and the stationary road surface. Vortices are created by the work done on the air stream and the overall effect on the pressure

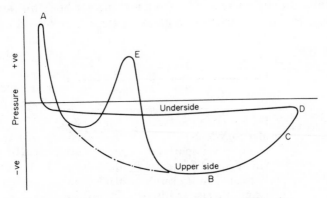

Fig 7.2   Pressure distribution over GT body.

that exists at different points along the undersurface depends to a large extent on the height of the underbody and the general slope from front to rear. With an upswept tail it is possible to create a depression towards the rear end of the underbody to counteract some of the lift exerted at **B**. When the ground clearance is higher at the front than at the rear it is possible for a pressure to be created underneath the car which is most undesirable since this augments the lift created at zone **B**. This lift increases with speed and at speeds of 150 m.p.h. upwards it is possible for this lift to be high enough to equal the static load on the rear wheels. Such a car becomes completely unstable at such speeds. Corrective treatment to regain stability at speed can take the form of a spoiler or projecting lip at the rear edge of the roof to create a downward pressure or an aerofoil may be mounted at the rear of the car. Finally, instead of corrective devices, we can design the body *ab initio* to hold the rear wheels firmly on the ground at speed. This modern concept of a 'wedge' body and the influence of aerofoils and spoilers will be the subject of a separate section of the chapter.

Drag

The resistance of the air to the forward movement of a body moving through it is called drag and is conventionally considered as the summation of two components, *'form drag'* and *'friction drag'*.

Form drag, in simple language, is the energy expended in pushing the air on one side. On a rectangular body we would deflect the air outwards to a greater extent than would occur

TABLE 7.1

Type of Car	C_d
Pre-war open sports car	0.6 –0.8
Modern saloon	0.45–0.55
Modern open sports car	0.50–0.60
Group 3 or 4 GT sports car	0.33–0.38
Formula 1 racing car	0.60–0.65
Group 5 racing sports car	0.35–0.50

if the body had an egg-like shape. The maximum form drag is created by pushing a flat plate, flat side forwards, through the air; the least by the teardrop shape we usually call, 'streamlined' with a length to breadth ratio of 2.5 to 1.

Friction drag is the resistance, in units of force, created in the layers of air adjacent to the surface of the body.

The total force that must be exerted on a body to overcome both form drag and friction drag is given by the following expresssion:

$$F = C_d \, A \, V^2 \text{ (in consistent units)}$$

where C_d is called the drag coefficient

A is the maximum cross-sectional area

V is the velocity.

Using the popular motoring units of V in m.p.h. and A in ft^2, the expression becomes:

$$F \text{ (lbs)} = \frac{C_d \, A \, V^2}{391}$$

The horsepower to overcome this drag, using the same units, is given by:

$$\text{Drag HP} = \frac{C_d \, A \, V^3}{146\,600}$$

Typical drag coefficients are given in Table 7.1

To show how far these bodies are from what we call true streamlining the above values should be compared with the values of $C_d = 0.03$ achieved by a perfectly streamlined shape.

It is of special significance that the power lost in drag varies as the cube of the speed. If a car needs 40 horse-power to overcome the air resistance at 90 m.p.h. it will need 8 times this, or 320 horse-power at 180 m.p.h. The power required to overcome rolling resistance however varies roughly as the square of the speed (very approximately since the tyre construction and profile ratio affects this index). Typical values for the rolling resistance would be 9 b.h.p. at 90 m.p.h. and 32 b.h.p. at 180 m.p.h.

To achieve an increase in maximum speed of 5 per cent the designer has three alternatives:

(a) a reduction in the frontal area (maximum cross-section) of 5 per cent.
(b) a reduction in the drag coefficient of 5 per cent.
(c) an increase in the engine power of about 16 per cent.

From this it would seem more sensible to concentrate on a reduction in the frontal area (as Bugatti did) or an improvement in the drag coefficient (which Bugatti attempted to do in 1923 with his tank-like 2-litre straight-eight 'streamlined' Grand Prix entries for the French Grand Prix at Tours). An increase in engine power is usually feasible, but is often accompanied by a loss in reliability.

At the speeds of modern racing sports cars it is essential to provide either closed bodywork, or curved screens that give so much wrap-round that the effect is almost that of an enclosed body with an opening at the rear. An enclosed bubble canopy over the driver of fully streamlined profile gives the lowest drag figures, even when due allowance is made for the internal drag losses of the air ducts required for ventilation. Minimum body and screen widths and depths, seating dimensions and seat to roof heights, as defined in Appendix J must of course be met, and when we have complied with these regulations and provided a body to enclose the rest of the mechanism there is really only one factor left for experimentation, namely the drag coefficient. Unfortunately we can seldom change this without also changing the lift coefficient and if the car is to be controllable at speeds we cannot ignore lift.

Drag and Lift Coefficients

As shown diagrammatically in Fig 7.1 the sum of the drag forces act horizontally at the C.G., while the lift forces act vertically. Knowing the value of the frontal area and the velocity at which these forces have been measured we can calculate the drag and lift coefficients:

$$C_d = \frac{F_d}{A\ V^2}$$

$$C_1 = \frac{F_1}{A\ V^2}$$

where

C_d is the Drag Coefficient
C_1 is the Lift Coefficient
F_d is the horizontal force (measured in the wind tunnel)
F_1 is the vertical force (measured in the wind tunnel).

For a typical GT car the pressure distribution over the body would be something like the pattern shown in Fig 7.2. Since more area lies below the atmospheric pressure than above, the summation of all vertical forces will be upwards, i.e. a lift. This lift is biased towards the rear. If we were to remove the re-entrant curve produced by the bonnet top and the screen by a plastic moulding, as indicated in Fig 7.1 by a chain-dotted line, we would not only increase the lift, but we would move the center of action of this negative pressure further forwards. The drag would therefore be reduced at the expense of an increase in lift. This is an indication of the sort of decision that must be taken by aerodynamicists today when the interaction between drag and lift becomes so crucial at speeds above 200 m.p.h.

Intuitive Streamlining

Many of the early attempts at streamlining were inspired guesses. Even the aeroplanes of the period had a relatively high drag. When the competition looks rather like a Victorian bedstead one only needs a rudimentary knowledge of aerodynamics to produce a racing car with lower drag coefficient. Some pre-1914 racing cars had rudimentary tails, but the need to carry two spare wheels hardly helped the streamlining at the rear. The 1914 GP Mercedes appeared with a wedge shaped radiator, which was new for the Marque. This, it was supposed would help to cleave a path through the air at speed. Around the two spare wheels the tail had a modest curvature and, of great importance, there was a full-length underpan below the body. Several racing cars appeared during this era with a long pointed front to the radiator header tank and a rather odd afterthought on the front axle of the 1914 GP Vauxhall was the fitting of streamlined wooden fairings to the front axle beam. In this pre-1914 period the Coupe de l'Auto 3-litre Sunbeams with their narrow cowled radiators and long pointed tails were among the best examples of the state of the art at that time.

In the same year as the first futile attempt by Bugatti to produce a streamlined car there also appeared a grotesque Voisin of 'aerodynamic' shape. The intake duct alone must have added more drag than the rest of the body. It is significant that these amateurs in this new field failed so miserably in applying the new techniques learned from the field of aviation. When *le patron* stopped trying to be scientific he produced such elegant masterpieces as the Type 35 Bugatti (1924-30) and in America, those two wonderful engineers, Fred Duesenberg and Harry Miller, without a scrap of scientific training to help them made remarkably low drag single-seater Indianapolis race cars with simple curved radiator cowls, the narrowest of bodies and magnificent tapered tails. Everything else, of course, was hanging out; the wheels, the axles, even the drivers elbows. Nevertheless the results proved how successful the formula was at that time. Frank Lockhart in 1927 on a Miller Special fitted with a 1.5-litre (91 in^3) supercharged engine and running on normal gasoline achieved a flying mile of 164 m.p.h. The frontal area was only 8.8 ft^2 and the body was well streamlined by standards of the time.

As speeds gradually increased more and more of the mechanism and the driver had to be enclosed. The frontal area inevitably increased and the scientific lessons of aero-dynamics began to be absorbed into the general technology of automobile engineering.

WIND TUNNELS

One can apply much of the knowledge that aircraft research workers have accumulated over the last half-century to the initial design layout of a new body, but the final stages of development, before a body is committed to the prototype stage, are taken in the wind tunnel. As long ago as 1960 Peter Kyropoulus of General Motors Styling Staff made the following comments:

'For high speed cars (racing) I consider it foolish not to get complete tunnel data. The average passenger car can get by nicely without it, and many do. There is however, a difference between getting by and doing well. The more we learn about the interaction between car and air, the better off we are in planning new designs'.

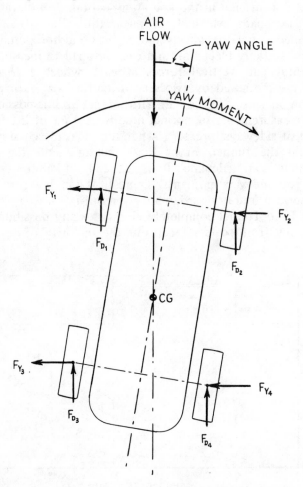

Fig 7.3 The Ford Motor Company's Full-Scale Wind Tunnel at Detroit: How forces are recorded in the horizontal plane. Four 'levapads' are used to indicate forces in the vertical plane.

The majority of wind tunnel testing uses small scale models to make measurements of the drag and lift forces and of the disturbing forces when the car is pitching or is running at an angle of yaw to the direction of the airflow. Some of the larger manufacturers have built wind tunnels large enough to test full-size cars. The Ford Motor Company Wind Tunnel in Detroit which went into operation in 1958 is 20 ft wide and 12 ft 6 in high in the operating section. Four 'levapads', which are pads which float on a thin film of air, are positioned under the wheels and vertical and horizontal load cells are suitably placed around each levapad to measure the horizontal and vertical forces at each wheel. Horizontal forces are measured by two sets of load cells at each wheel position, as shown in Fig 7.3. With this set-up it is possible to make measurements of normal drag forces, F_d of lift forces F_l and of sideways forces, F_y when the car is placed at a yaw angle in the tunnel. From these measurements the aerodynamicist can calculate drag, lift and lateral forces and pitch, roll and yaw moments. Typical lift and drag forces for an American four-door sedan are given in Fig 7.4.

The Ford Tunnel completely eliminates any possibility of inaccuracy from scale effects, but the majority of develop-

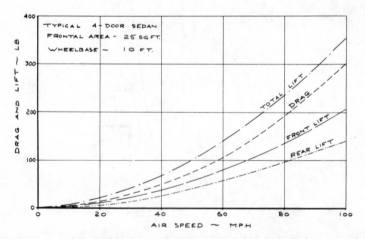

Fig 7.4 Typical lift and drag measurements made in the Ford Full-Scale Wind Tunnel.

ment work on competition cars is carried out on scale models to save expense. In constructing the model great care is taken to achieve, not only geometric similarity, but also dynamic similarity. The external volume of a one-tenth scale model would of course be $1/10^3$ or one-thousandth that of the original. The weight, however would have to be $1/10^2$ and the moment of inertia $1/10^4$ to achieve true dynamic similarity. This presents problems to the model makers, but they usually make a very close approach to these conditions.

Flow Patterns

Even without a wind tunnel we can learn the general pattern of the air flow over the surface of a body and make an estimate of the velocities in certain regions. The wool-tuft method has been used for many years, while other laboratories have developed methods using special quick-drying paints or lamp-black dispersed on kerosene. Even when using these methods the availability of a wind tunnel helps to save time. The wool-tufts method calls for the body surface to be covered by several hundred short strands of wool which are glued to the surface at one end only. Still photographs are taken to indicate the direction of air flow at these hundreds of points all over the body at different speeds. The presence of turbulence, i.e. eddies in the airstream, and the extent of this turbulence is indicated by blurring of the still photograph, but the use of a high speed movie camera will give a better indication of the extent of these eddies. The technique using lamp black in kerosene or special quick drying paints calls for the surface to be covered by hundreds of small circular dots. The spread of these over the surface under the airflow is a rough measure of the direction and extent of the air movement.

Boundary Layer Separation

It is well known that a thin layer of air can remain undisturbed close to the surface itself, even at fairly high speeds. A car with a coating of dust on the top of the bonnet can be driven for many miles without this layer being disturbed. We call this the 'boundary layer' and in certain circumstances this boundary layer can be caused to separate

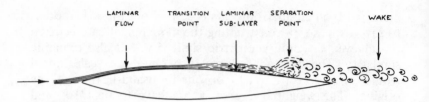

Fig 7.5   Air flow pattern over the upper surface of an aerofoil.

from the surface. When separation occurs the surface drag per unit area increases drastically for all parts of the body aft to the point of separation. Fig 7.5 shows how this separation occurs when air flows over a typical aerofoil, such as a section of an aeroplane wing. For clarity the thickness of the boundary layer is exaggerated. At first the boundary layer is very thin and is completely *laminar.* By this we mean that successive layers of air slide at a slightly higher speed over the next with no eddying of molecules from one layer to the next. The innermost layer is of course at zero velocity relative to the surface and the outermost layer is at 99 per cent of the free air velocity.

Even though the surface is perfectly smooth and unbroken by rivet heads or other surface irregularities it is not possible to prolong the laminar flow all the way from the leading edge to the trailing edge, except at very low velocities. The molecules in each layer inevitably collide and interact to produce an interchange of energy between layers. At some point downstream of the leading edge small eddies begin to circulate within the outer layers of the boundary layer, even though the sub-layer is still laminar. Where this turbulence within the boundary layer first begins is called the *transition point.* After the transition point the boundary layer increases in thickness, rising to as much as an inch or so, depending upon the velocity. Further downstream the turbulence increases until, when the layer in contact with the surface becomes turbulent, we have reached what is called the *separation point,* since the boundary layer can now be said to have separated from the surface. Downstream of the separation point the wing surface is no longer protected by a laminar layer and the scrubbing action of the turbulent air

causes a large increase in drag. Naturally the aerodynamicist
tries to delay the onset of separation.

Separation occurs much more readily in a region of falling
pressure. Thus it tends to occur sooner on a fat aerofoil than
on one of very thin section. In the same way the roof line of
a car should not fall too steeply if early separation of the
boundary layer is to be avoided.

The study of air patterns on a wide range of body shapes
has disclosed several interesting phenomena.

Vortices

Any discontinuity in the convexity of the body shape can
lead to flow separation. Separation of the boundary layer
produces vortices and these can be small, of the size we see in
water when we move a finger through it, or as big in diameter
as the car itself. If the slope of the windscreen is too close to
the vertical and certainly if it is not generously curved in
planform the boundary layer will separate from the bonnet
top, even though this is not a region of falling pressure. The
boundary layer can be re-established again on the roof of the

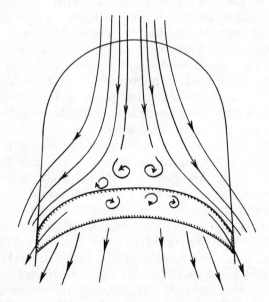

Fig 7.6a   Air flow in plan and around traditional windscreen.

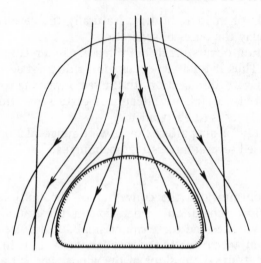

Fig 7.6b   Airflow in plan over and around a spherical-profile windscreen.

car, but the region shown at E in Fig 7.1 will be a region of
turbulent eddies, the vortex motion being caused by the
scrubbing action of the main airstream on the relatively
stagnant air trapped against the screen. An approach to a
quarter spherical screen shape as shown in plan view in Fig
7.6b and a rake of at least 45° to the screen in elevation is the
usual method adopted to remove this region of high drag.
Since this is a region of rising pressure the tendency to
separation at this point is not as difficult to cure as the
separation problem on the falling roof line.

    Eddy formation on the roof and at the rear of a car is a
problem that has occupied research workers since Professor
W. Kamm wrote his classic book on body design (Das
Kraftfahrzeug) before the last war. On a typical saloon (see
Fig 7.7) it occurs near the top edge of the rear window and
becomes magnified in the turbulent wake of the car itself.
One popular trick to re-entrain the boundary layer and
reduce the total cross-section of the turbulent wake is the
provision of a lip or spoiler on the top edge of the boot or on
GT cars like the Aston Martin at the rearmost point of the
sloping roof. Depending upon the dimensions of this lip it

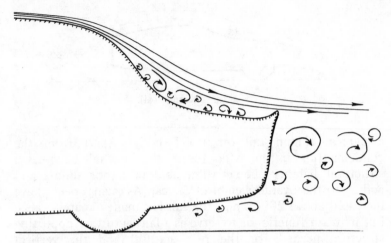

Fig 7.7   Re-entrainment of boundary layer by spoiler on boot (trunk) of typical passenger car.

can serve a dual purpose if so desired. In the case of the Aston Martin it is large enough to exert a downward pressure to reduce aerodynamic lift at speed.

When the science of aerodynamics was first applied to the automobile there were many attempts to produce the perfectly streamlined tail, a tail in fact that would produce no vortex formation. This is very difficult to achieve in a region of falling pressure as must occur when the cross-section of the body is being reduced. A close approach to a fully streamlined tail would be given by one with a conical shape having a half-angle of no more than 7.5°. This of course would have a ridiculous length and the additional surface added to the car would largely offset the reduction in form drag by an increase in friction drag. Professor Kamm demonstrated that a sharply cut-off tail, what we now call a 'Kamm tail' is a very effective compromise. Professor Kamm showed that the Law of Diminishing Returns begins to operate after we have reduced the car cross-sectional area by about 50 per cent of the maximum. The reduction in form drag hardly offsets the increase in friction drag if the tail is made much longer, so said the Professor with a fine Teutonic logic, let us just chop off the tail at this point. Fig 7.8 shows

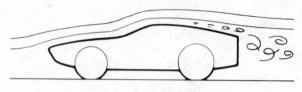

Fig 7.8   Kamm Tail.

a typical Kamm tail on a GT body. Apart from the condemnation in the wind tunnel the long tail becomes a structural liability, being vulnerable in minor shunts and adding to the overall weight of the car. As racing speeds have increased above 200 m.p.h. the tail has made a reappearance but its main function is to serve as a fairing of the supporting structure needed for the rear aerofoil and the vertical stabilising fins that are used to assist stability at high speed, in the manner of the flights on a dart.

The more observant type of motorist (and our reader is surely one of these) will have noticed that the exhaust gases emerging from the tail pipe or pipes of a car, when made visible by condensed vapour on a cold morning, will always form spiral vortices in the wake of the car. Viewed from the rear a right-hand pipe will produce an anti-clockwise swirl, a left-hand pipe a clockwise swirl. The cause of this is an upward movement of air over the sides of the car into the low pressure zone on the roof. Even when the pressure below the car is negative it is always at a much higher pressure relative to that above the car. The forward motion of the car converts this upward flow into two large spirals which meet behind the car to exert an influence on the turbulent wake. Some *avant garde* body stylists, such as the Italian Bertone, have produced custom-bodied cars with inward curving fins that extend rearwards across the tail and are claimed to prevent this vortex formation. How much this reduces drag is not known but the reduction in rear vision is very evident.

Internal Ducting

Radiators, engine air intakes, brake and cockpit cooling ducts all add to the total drag losses on a vehicle. Every duct has an entry loss which can be kept to a minimum by drawing air from an area of low turbulence and by the actual shape of the entry. In addition there are further losses from the frictional drag of the walls of the ducts and from turbulence losses caused by bends and changes in cross-sectional area in the duct. In the case of coolant and oil radiators the resistance to flow across the radiator matrices adds to the total drag forces exerted on the car.

The Influence of the Road Surface

We cannot ignore the effect of the road surface on the flow pattern around the car body. In the wind tunnel testing we are concerned with obtaining a true simulation of road conditions and it would appear that the closest approach might be given by placing a stationary model on a flat conveyor belt which is moving backwards at the same speed as the air in the tunnel and by rotating the road wheels by means of this same belt. As reported by Kent, Kyropoulis and Tanner (S.A.E. Progress Report on Aerodynamics No. SP180) the effect on the measured drag coefficient of a staionary ground plane and non-rotating wheels is not very great and that no great error will be introduced by this much simpler method. The drag coefficients measured on a fifth-scale model of an American sedan are given below.

TABLE 7.2
Influence on Drag Coefficient of Ground Plane

Model set-up	C_d
Fixed ground plane	0.538
Fixed ground plane, running wheels	0.530
Running belt, fixed wheels	0.515
Running belt, running wheels	0.515

The wheels are well enclosed in a modern American sedan. If the experiment were to be repeated on a model of a GP car with its very wide exposed wheels a much wider divergence in the readings would almost certainly be found. We however are concerned with racing sports cars, where the wheels are enclosed, although perhaps not as effectively as on a modern passenger car.

The influence of the ground plane itself can be very great on the airflow and on the lift forces on a car. Workers in this field have in general avoided the complication of a moving conveyor belt in the floor of their wind tunnels. The majority of the testing has been carried out on passenger cars with relatively high ground clearances. This is not applicable to racing sports cars today where the ground clearance is very close to the F.I.A. specified minimum of 10 cm (3.94 inches). An interesting series of experiments were carried out and reported in 1965 by Joseph J. Cornish III of the Aerophysics Department of Mississippi State University describing some interesting lift effects on cylinders and elliptical sections when placed at different distances from the ground plane. When a cylinder is placed in the wind tunnel and is gradually brought closer to the ground plane there is at first a small downward pull (negative lift) towards the ground plane. This is caused by the venturi effect of the air flowing under the curved surface of the cylinder. This pull increases slightly until at some point close to $h/r = 2$ (see Fig 7.9) this downward pull very rapidly becomes an upward lift and at the point where the cylinder actually touches the ground

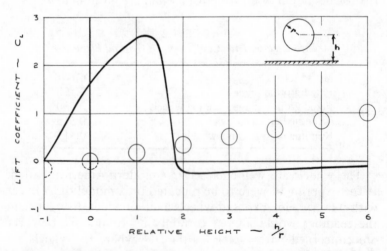

Fig 7.9   Lift exerted by airstream on a cylindrical section at different distances from the ground (*After Joseph J. Cornish*).

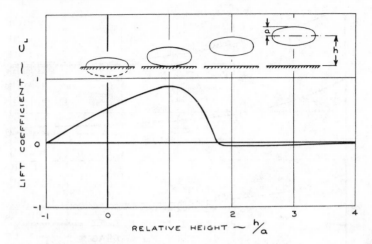

Fig 7.10   Lift exerted by airstream on an elliptical section at different distances from the ground (*After Joseph J. Cornish*).

plane the lift coefficient reaches a maximum value of C_l = 2.6. The actual point of zero lift is a function of air velocity and the surface roughness. As the cylinder sinks below the surface of the ground plane, as one would expect, the lift coefficient falls.

Fig 7.10 shows that an elliptical section with major to minor axis ratio of 2.5 also has a sharp transition from negative to positive lift at a similar distance from the ground plane. The maximum lift in this case is much reduced since an ellipse has lower form drag. It is not unreasonable to carry the analogy a little further and anticipate that a similar critical ground clearance will exist in the case of an automobile.

Many experiments on car models and in recent years on full-scale passenger cars confirm that an optimum road clearance giving maximum lift does occur on the majority of vehicles. These experiments suggest that the lift coefficient of many modern cars could be reduced simply by fitting larger diameter wheels. This is not, of course, a very practical solution since the raising of the centre of gravity would introduce other undesirable effects.

A reduction of lift is almost invariably accompanied by an

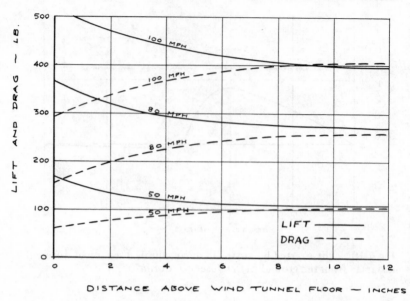

Fig 7.11   Effect of vehicle elevation above wind tunnel floor on drag and lift forces on a typical American sedan.

increase in drag. Fig 7.11 shows how these two coefficients change when the ground clearance under a full-size American sedan is increased by as much as 12 inches above normal. Since the normal ground clearance would be about 7 inches, however this does not tell us what happens at ground clearances as low as 4 inches.

We have shown that the lift on an aerofoil section or a circular section reaches a maximum when it just touches or has a negligible clearance from the ground, yet with a fairly large ground clearance the venturi effect produces the opposite effect of a negative lift. The phenomenon demonstrated in Figs 7.9 and 7.10 will be more clearly understood when it is seen that the flow underneath the cylinder or elliptical section will begin to fall in velocity very rapidly as the section nearly touches the ground plane. The flow underneath the section creates a depression which varies as V^2 (by Bernoulli's Law). Thus a drop in velocity of 50 per cent will reduce this depression to a quarter of its maximum value. As the section touches the surface the flow underneath ceases and the only forces remaining are the lift forces created by the air flow over the curved upper surface. This then is a good indication of the probable behaviour of the air forces acting on a sports car with a low ground clearance and a convex underbody. But what happens when the car is fitted with a completely flat underpan and the clearance is held down to a minimum of 4 inches?

There is no simple answer but the work of Joseph J. Cornish on simple half-cylinder sections suggested that the use of spoilers at front and rear can be used to modify the lift on such a car. A spoiler at the front of a half-cylinder reduces lift (see Fig 7.12) and one at the rear increases it. The effect of a front spoiler was much enhanced if separation of the boundary layer occurred early, as indicated by point X in the diagram. If we apply a little common sense to these results we soon see that the effect of the rear spoiler is to trap air underneath the car, neglecting the air that spills out at the sides. This converts some of the kinetic energy of the airstream into pressure energy which pushes upwards on the underside of the car. If the only effective access to the clearance space is from the rear, as when a full-width front spoiler reaches down to the road surface, the pressure under the car becomes negative since this is the condition of the car's wake. With good streamlining and a late separation point (such as Y in Fig 7.12) the depression under the body will be relatively low, while the upper surface lift will be high. For such a car the front spoiler will be less effective. A typical racing sports car with a mid-engine location and all the turbulence created in the wake of its rear aerofoil will have

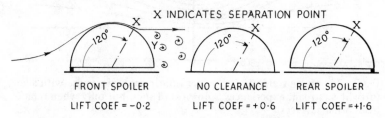

Fig 7.12   Influence of spoiler on lift (*After Joseph J. Cornish*).

a very early separation point and a fairly high depression in its wake. Such a car will benefit in a two-fold way from the use of a full-width spoiler at the front. The spoiler will not only present an inclined upper face to the airstream to increase the downthrust on the front wheels, but it will also act as a partial restrictor of air flow into the underbody space, thus reducing the pressure below the car. Even though the spoiler must be given the requisite ground clearance less air will be admitted from the leading edge than would occur if the spoiler were omitted. An interesting experiment would be the use of two or three cascaded spoilers.

Wheel Rotation and Magnus Effect

Magnus effect is usually seen by the followers of ball games in the swerving flight of a baseball or a sliced golf ball and in the vertical plane as the drop effect of a tennis ball served with top spin. Fig 7.13 demonstrates how this occurs. With anti-clockwise rotations as shown, the effect of passing an airstream over a rotating cylinder (or to a reduced extent over a rotating sphere) is to slow down the airstream as it

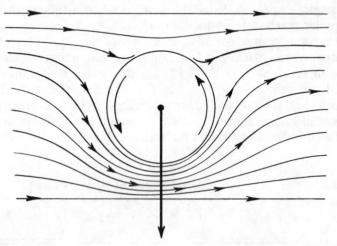

Fig 7.13   Magnus effect. A cylinder rotating anti-clockwise with a left to right airstream experiences a downward pull, but only when remote from other surfaces.

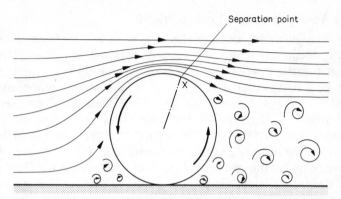

Fig 7.14   The air flow over an exposed road wheel (as on a Formula 1 car). The presence of the road surface destroys the Magnus effect.

passes across the top of the cylinder and speed it up as it traverses the lower suface. By Bernoulli's Law the reduction in velocity near the upper surface results in an increase in pressure. Below the cylinder there is a corresponding reduction in pressure. A downward force is thus created, the magnitude of which depends upon the speed of rotation and upon the speed of the airstream. It is sometimes suggested that the Magnus effect creates a downthrust against the road surface on a rotating car wheel and that this is particularly high in the case of the wide section tyres used on racing cars. For the Magnus effect to occur it would be necessary for air to be flowing underneath the wheels. Moreover the road surface must wipe off the boundary layer most effectively at the contact patch (see Fig 7.14) and the turbulent region in the wake of the wheel is certainly not conducive to the rapid establishment of a stable boundary layer. At the top of the wheel then the boundary layer, such as it is, must still be turbulent in character. Not only will this nullify any Magnus effect, but the normal lift effect that occurs when air flows over a convex surface will also be largely destroyed by the turbulent conditions near the upper surface of the wheel. The overall effect of an exposed rotating road wheel must therefore be that of a very slight lift.

The Aerodynamics of Locked Wheels

It is intriguing to consider the change in lift coefficient that must occur when a wide section exposed wheel suddenly stops rotating, under the action of excessively fierce braking. A wheel that is sliding along the ground is largely represented by the case of $h/r = 1$ in Fig 7.9. There is, of course, a difference in that the ground plane is in this case moving backwards in relation to the cylindrical section, but it has been shown in the experiments reported in Table 7.2 that the movement of the ground plane had only a minor effect on the drag coefficient. It is reasonable to assume that ground plane movement will also have little effect on the lift coefficient. As soon as a freely rotating wheel locks the laminar boundary layer will be quickly established over the front and upper surfaces of the tyre. Separation will occur at some point immediately behind the top of the wheel (indicated at X in Fig 7.15) and, since the ground plane is moving across the skidding contact patch, a small area in the region of Y will have its laminar boundary layer broken up by eddy formation.

For such a condition one would predict a lift coefficient of at least 1.5 for a typical racing tyre pattern and a little higher value for a smooth dry-weather tyre. The prospect is alarming since it indicates that a Formula 1 car with front or rear wheels locked under hard braking at 75 m.p.h. will suddenly have a lift created of as much as 150 lb at the rear or 90 lb if the front wheels lock. If only one rear wheel locks the

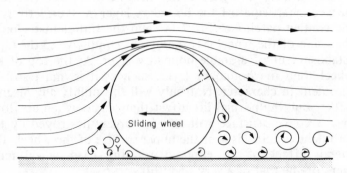

Fig 7.15   Change in air flow pattern with a locked road wheel.

unbalanced lift at the rear will probably provoke a spin. What better argument can we present for the fitting of anti-locking devices to the braking systems on Grand Prix cars?

If for no other reason the unpredictable behaviour of exposed wide wheels at speed, especially if they should lose contact with the road on a switchback straight, is a strong inducement to enclose them inside the bodywork. On a Group 5 racing sports car it is necessary for the mudguard (or the part of the body serving as a mudguard) to cover at least a third of the circumference and to extend to the full width of the tyre. With enclosed bodywork it is quite possible to reduce the drag coefficient by such a large percentage that the increase in frontal area becomes of minor importance. For obvious reasons one must provide adequate body clearance above the wheels for full bump movement and for minimum drag from the centifugal action of the wheel rotation inside a partially closed housing one should try to provide the same clearance all round the wheel arch. The rear of the wheel arch is often non-existent since this helps the body designer to make a smooth blending-in of the inner face of the wheel arch with the outer contours of the body side.

AEROFOILS

Apart from the use of horizontal stabilizing fins on land speed record cars the first attempt to apply aerofoils set at a negative angle of incidence (with the leading edge lower that the trailing edge) was seen at the Nürburgring in 1956 when Michael May used one in practice for the 1000 km Sports Car Race on a Porsche Spyder. The scrutineers rejected the device as dangerous and the next appearance of an aerofoil in an event of any significance was in the Can-Am Series of sports car races in 1966 when Jim Hall fitted a large aerofoil high above the rear end of the Chaparrel Type 2E.

As related by Hap Sharp, a member of the Chaparrel team, the need for an aerofoil grew out of the instability of the car at its top speed, but the use of the aerofoil to improve cornering power could have been in Jim Hall's mind from the start. The adjustable aerofoil which appeared in 1967 on the Type 2F was certainly used with a much higher angle of negative incidence when cornering than when running at high speed. The aerofoil was mounted high above the car and was carried on two sturdy struts attached to the rear wheel hub carriers. The angle of incidence could be controlled by means of a third pedal in the cockpit (no clutch pedal being necessary since the Chaparrel was fitted with automatic transmission) and with this system it was soon evident that the use of the aerofoil not only improved stability at speed by increasing the load on the rear wheels, but also increased cornering power in medium and high speed bends with the negative incidence at a greater angle. Mike Spence actually tried reducing the angle of incidence to zero while in the middle of the Mulsanne Corner at Le Mans. The resulting slide convinced him that the aerofoil really did work.

The cornering force generated by a tyre at a given slip angle is a function of the load on the tyre. Thus if we take as a typical case a racing tyre running at a slip angle of 8° and generating a cornering force of 330 lb with a tyre load of 300 lb (which with balanced loading on all tyres represented a centrifugal acceleration of 1.1 g) and we then use an aerofoil to apply an additional downthrust of 90 lb per tyre the cornering force will be increased to about 420 lb at the same slip angle (a centrifugal acceleration of about 1.4 g).

It is now customary to use short aerofoils or combination spoiler/flaps at the front of the body, but the width and height of all aerofoils were drastically curtailed by the FIA in an attempt to remove the obvious hazards introduced by the flimsy structures that were raced by some competitors (and which collapsed in several cases). Aerofoils must now be mounted on the body, not directly on the hub carriers, since this reduces the shock loads transmitted to the supporting structure.

The practice of 'slipstreaming', i.e. 'getting a tow' as it is sometimes called, by following in the wake of a slightly more powerful competitor on the straight is fraught with even more danger when aerofoils are used since, the turbulent air in the wake of the leading car reduces the effectiveness of the aerofoil on the following car. This can be particularly troublesome when a straight is followed by a fast bend.

The Keil Profile

The current body profile seen today on Formula 1 cars and on several racing sports cars is that of a wedge. In this way we are able to incorporate a nose that penetrates the air with as little disturbance as possible of the boundary layer on the upper surface and at the same time to present an angled upper surface that will provide a vertical pressure component to assist in holding the rear end of the car down to the road surface at high speed. At cornering speeds this downward thrust is very much reduced and the wedge body has not yet made the aerofoil obsolete.

An interesting development from Raleigh, North Carolina is the Porsche-Keil sports car (*Keil* being German for Wedge). The principle of the variable wedge body used on the Porsche-Keil is shown in Fig. 7.16. A hydraulic ram is used to lift the rear end of the body relative to the chassis frame. In this way the angle of incidence of the body can be varied from a normal angle of 7° up to as much as 20°. This angle of incidence can be controlled by a lever in the cockpit and the whole operation takes 2 seconds. No doubt the use of a larger capacity hydraulic pump would reduce this time lag to about half a second if thought desirable. With sound engineering of such a body there is no reasonable objection that a scrutineer could present to disqualify it from international events. Presumably the car passed Technical Inspection in the local sports car races in which it was successfully raced by its designer Mr William Eichelberger.

Fig. 7.16 The 'Keil' principle; the use of a variable-angle wedge-profile body as used on the Porsche-Keil sports car.

The Chaparrel Fan-Suction Car

One must admire Jim Hall for his ingenuity. Unfortunately, his latest method for creating downthrust was finally rejected by the F.I.A. in December 1970, but not before he had demonstrated how well he could show a clean pair of fans to the opposition. The Chaparrel Type 2J used an auxiliary engine to drive two fans situated in the Kamm tail which created a suction inside a well-sealed underbody section of about 62 ft^2 Over this large area a fan suction of only 4 inches head of water (0.145) lb/in^2) will give a total downthrust of 1300 lb and this force, unlike that created by aerodynamic devices, can be applied to the car when stationary! This car appeared in three races before the F.I.A. ban and the rate of acceleration from the starting-line was most impressive, since it was achieved without the customary black marks in the road.

To maintain suction below the car called for a system of retractable skirts on the sides and front of the suction area. The suspension system was also designed to cope with the downthrust of 1300 lb which was half the weight of the car itself. The front skirt, devised by an ex-Chevrolet engineer, Don Gates, used a double set of hinged plastic plates that rose and fell automatically as the ground clearance changed. The development costs were close to a million dollars and apart from the danger of throwing small stones at anyone in the slipstream (and nobody has banned tyres yet for doing just that) there is nothing intrinsically unsafe in the fan-suction racing car. The jet turbine car has an even larger turbulent slipstream of very hot gases and if this discourages the art of 'slip-streaming' it will help the sport by removing a dangerous practice from the scene.

One must sympathise with the committee members of the F.I.A. who carry such heavy responsibilities in administering the rules of the sport, but a small degree of latitude should be allowed to encourage the efforts of the more imaginative racing car designers if we are not to see the approach of mental atrophy in future racing car designs. Do we really believe that *Racing improves the Breed* - or is it all just another way of selling cigarettes and after- shave lotion?

CHAPTER EIGHT
Frame and Body

Tradition

The frame, or chassis, as we once called it, need not necessarily be constructed as a separate structural entity from the body. Since the body must be attached to the frame the two units inevitably interact one upon the other when the car is in motion. To illustrate this we can consider some of the more badly engineered examples from the past. In all fairness we cannot exempt all vintage sports cars from our examples. The use of a simple steel ladder type frame and a lightly constructed timber-framed body was the continuance of tradition, the tradition established in the carriage trade. One could say that the change from a wood frame to a steel frame was an innovation but in general it was not what one might call 'revolutionary'.

The ladder frame was usually made from channel sections joined by rivetted gussets, plates and angles and was usually so flexible and lacking in torsional resistance that the body builder was forced to use very heavy ash sections in the framework of his body — sometimes as heavy as 4 inches by 2 inches in the sills — to protect his body against undue flexure. Despite all the efforts of these fine craftsmen a door would occasionally jam shut if the car was parked on uneven ground.

The object lesson is simple. The body and frame, however constructed, must be regarded structurally as a single unit. Why then, asks our nimble-witted reader, do we not construct the body and frame as a single unit in the first place? The answer is that we sometimes do just that.

Monocoque Construction

It would be naïve to assume that the unification of frame and body into a single shell (monocoque means like a single egg shell) is easy or is the perfect solution. The idea is old. To the

133

best of my knowledge it was first used by Vincenzo Lancia on the 1922 Lancia, but there could be earlier examples (Bill Boddy of 'Motor Sport' will no doubt mention them when he reads his review copy). If we could simplify the whole shape to something approaching that of an egg and if we were not called upon to mount inside this egg such heavy loads as engines and fuel tanks and drivers, and at the same time cut large holes in the surface of the egg to provide doors and windscreen frames and detachable covers to provide access to the engine and other mechanical components it would be a true monocoque. With all these conflicting requirements it becomes a compromise. The Formula 1 solution is usually called 'semi-monocoque' since the typical design has a centre section that is more like a bath-tub than an egg. The driver is seated, or more precisely is half-reclining, between two main longitudinal structural members which house, ominously, the compartmented flexible-bag fuel tanks. In the cars powered by the Cosworth DFV engine, the engine is bolted directly to the bulkhead behind the driver and the engine acts as a stressed member of the frame and is designed to have sufficient stiffness and strength for the rear suspension loads to be fed directly into it. Other designs use a tubular frame behind the driver to carry the engine, drivebox, oil tank and cooler and the mounting brackets for the rear suspension links. In nearly all current designs a similar tubular structure is used as an extension forwards of the bath-tub front bulkhead to carry the front suspension and any other components that the designer chooses to locate there.

Unitized Construction

The popular mass-produced car, with a few exceptions among the largest American sedans, has had a unitized construction of body and frame for many years, although the frame is still discernable in many examples in the form of welded box sections in the plane of the car floor. The torsional stiffness from these unitized cars usually comes from the fabricated bulkheads and other complex fabricated components that make up the structure of what we would have called the body-frame forty years ago. The whole structure is so complex that it defies the most sophisticated methods of stress analysis, despite the availability of numerous computers and experienced programmers. The designer of a unitized body-frame takes refuge in that well-known 'factor of ignorance' that engineers have used since the time of Leonardo da Vinci and the usual production design is inevitably heavier than the perfect design would be. It is of course impossible for the designer to include in such calculations that he may make an exact allowance for the variable quality of production spot welding. It is this production line variability that makes the American stock car driver and the European rally entrant have his car 'double-welded' at all accessible structural joints before putting his life at risk.

Specialised sports cars made in limited numbers can have very strict control of all welding operations and a meticulous inspection system. Even higher standards are possible when Group 5 prototypes are under construction. Yet the design factor of ignorance remains. Some parts of the structure are less highly stressed than others, simply through the inability of the designer to analyse the stresses in the structure accurately. When he has actually made the vehicle he can use all manner of techniques to measure the stresses in the various key areas and with careful inspection after road testing (plus an element of luck) he can spot incipient cracks or the start of buckling in an overstressed section before the driver is put at risk.

Manufacturers of prototype racing sports cars are often faced with the same problems of last-minute modifications as those that face the development teams working on a true prototype of a production car. After months of almost endless road-testing and hundred of hours of rig testing it becomes imperative to change the design of one component, such as moving an inboard brake location to an outboard position to obtain adequate brake cooling or changing the dimensions of a rear aerofoil to improve cornering. Such modifications have a nasty habit of being successful in themselves, but at the same time creating serious havoc in another component. The increased down thrusts created by the improved design of aerofoil could for example cause a failure in the attachment bracket of a rear suspension link.

This highlights one of the weaknesses of the unitized body/frame construction. The system does not lend itself to simple design modifications. This no doubt is the reason why the tubular welded steel frame is still so popular. Nothing could be so adaptable.

Stressed-skin Construction

The majority of aircraft made before the war were either covered in fabric or used the aluminium panels that formed the outer surface purely as a means of achieving the required profile. A more imaginative designer, such as R. J. Mitchell, who designed the Spitfire, had already proved on his Schneider Trophy racing seaplanes that the lightest construction for a given weight of material is given when the outer skin is made to share a proportion of the total stresses in the whole structure. From this idea, after the usual conservative proving period of twenty years or so, the stressed skin principle is now accepted as a sound basis for the design of racing sports cars.

From the start we must recognize that the major problems that have arisen in applying the principle to racing car design are only met when an aircraft in landing and taking off. The structure of a car receives extremely concentrated loads from the attachment brackets of the suspension links. In the case of an aeroplane these impulse loads are very much softened by the large movements of the oleo legs, but a racing car has very limited suspension travel, a very hard suspension in fact. Accelerations as high as 3 g are quite possible from single wheel bumps and this means that a car weighing 2000 lb will have an instantaneous load of about three-quarters of a ton superimposed on the static loads already carried by the suspension mountings. Without careful design to spread this load over a wide area it is not difficult to see that the stressed skin in this region would develop fatigue cracks before the end of a single season. Additional structural members or stiffening plates can be used to spread the loads. A clever little trick in the Rover 2000 was the use of a cranked arm to feed the vertical front suspension loads backwards into a strengthened scuttle bulkhead. The pivot pin of the crank is, of course, heavily loaded, but not in a vertical direction.

Torsional Stiffness

Torsional stiffness, when applied to a frame or unitized body/frame is usually expressed in units of lb-ft per degree of twist. As an example the torsional stiffness of the Ford GT40, Mark I, made up as an integrated box section structure from 0.024 inch and 0.028 inch sheet steel by brazed and spot-welded joints (and without the glass reinforced plastic body fitted) had a torsional stiffness of 12 500 lb-ft per degree. For comparison a Volkswagen 1500 unitized body shell gives a value of about 7000 lb-ft per degree.

The need to limit twist is not simply to make it easy to open and close the doors or even to reduce the level of flexing in the body panels. This in itself is a laudable goal when designing a Rolls-Royce Silver Shadow (10 800 lb-ft per degree over a wheelbase of almost 10 ft) but in a racing sports car the most devastating effect of a whippy frame is on the very critical suspension geometry. In Chapter Three we stressed the supreme importance of maintaining zero wheel camber on the outside wheel in a corner. With modern low-profile tyres this verticality must not vary by more than one degree on the front tyres and by no more than 3/4 of a degree on the wider rear tyres. A sudden change in the road surface, a ripple or a ridge, when taking a fast bend will disturb the dynamic loads on the four wheels. This in itself will call for correcting steering action. If however at the same time the frame suffers a twist of 1 to 1.5° there will be such a loss of tyre contact area at one or other corner of the car that the driver will probably lose control.

BODY DESIGN

The body on any high-speed racing car has a triple function. It must be ergonomically designed as a work room for the driver. It must also be designed as an aerodynamic shape to produce the required compromise between low-drag and good high-speed stability. Its third function is to contribute to the strength and stiffness of the complete structure. Depending upon the materials used and the method of construction this could be either a major or minor role.

The Cockpit

The dimensions of the compartment to carry the driver and the non-existent passenger to conform to Group 4, 5 or 7 rules must, of course, be no smaller than those specified in Appendix 'J' of the International Sporting Code. No designer is likely to exceed these dimensions by more than the odd inch or so and there is a real challenge in attempting to place the driver in the ideal position for all controls and switches to fall naturally into place. This in the language of modern technology is called 'ergonomics', the science of making work lighter. There is much that is traditional in driving a racing car. The brake and accelerator pedals are placed for convenient 'heeling and toeing', the traditional way of keeping the brakes applied while blipping the throttles for downward gear changes — easy enough for the expert when fit and fresh, but what an opportunity it presents to that gremlin we call 'chance' to make the driver's foot slip off a pedal as he drives at the razor edge of his limits when tiring after several hours of hard driving. There must be another way of blipping the throttle more ergonomic than this (a micro-switch on the gear lever? a rocking type of pedal?). Perhaps Louis Stanley of BRM who is so sincere in his efforts to reduce the hazards of motor racing will offer a prize for a satisfactory solution.

As an example of the dangers of fatigue, even among the fittest of drivers, we must remark on the number of races in the past that have been lost by one inadvertent act of 'over-revving'. The driver would usually shrug his shoulders and accept the full responsibility and the wrath of the team manager. Today it is normal for the ignition system to carry an over-speed cut-out device and the driver has one fewer thing to concern his over-worked brain.

Hans Mezger of Porsche KG defines the designer's task as follows: 'to create a car which will run a predetermined racing distance at a workable effort of the driver and without any risk to the driver's health in the shortest possible time'. Besides such fairly obvious requirements as easily operated pedals, steering and gear change lever, the correct positioning of the controls to suit the particular driver, the placing and easy readability of all instruments and warning lights, Dr

Mezger stresses the psychological influences of good car design: 'The real speed of a racing car is not primarily determined by the engine power and different kinds of driving resistance but by *the confidence of an experienced driver with a sense of responsibility in the car, expressed in the speed he dares to realise without risks*'. The author would insert the word 'unnecessary' before 'risks' since the only safe speed without risks is achieved by leaving the car in the garage. That is, undoubtedly, an excellent definition that Dr Mezger has given us of the designer's need to build in confidence. When perfect harmony is reached there is a centaur-like unity between driver and machine. Some drivers are more adaptive than others. Rodney Walkerley, former Sports Editor of 'The Motor', once told the author that Stirling Moss could never give an objective report on the road behaviour of a normal passenger car since he unconsciously adapted his driving to suit the particular handling weaknesses of the test car. A good road tester should be a little closer to the average driver. Jackie Stewart, like Stirling Moss, is a 'natural'. It sounds rather incredible for those of us who have to think as we drive, but Jackie Stewart claims to find Grand Prix driving 'so relaxing'. Unfortunately for the racing car designers there are not enough men of this calibre to go around. Even the best of conductors need to be fed with a constant supply of fresh, uncontaminated air, if they are not to lose the fine edge of their perception and constant alertness. Excessive vibration is known to induce fatigue and the driver must be insulated as much as possible from the lower frequency (less than 100 cycles per second) vibrations since these contribute most to the early onset of mental fatigue. As a last resort, if all else fails, one can always increase the thickness of the seat cushions.

The Aerodynamic Function

This second function of the body has been adequately covered in the previous chapter. Aerodynamics, however, do impinge upon the third function of the body since the forces induced by the air-flow are quite considerable and must be included in the stress calculations for the body. The long lightweight fibre-glass tails on some cars have been known to disintegrate at speed under an adverse combination of inertia and aerodynamic loads.

The Structural Function

Even when the main structural loads, from the inertia of the engine, transmission components, radiators, fuel tanks, driver's seat, etc. are all transmitted directly to the main frame, the body is not entirely unstressed since it must resist the loads imposed by its own inertia and by the aerodynamic forces around it. Moreover, as we stated at the beginning of the chapter, there must always be some interaction between body and frame since neither is completely inflexible.

The elastic modulus of the material or materials plays a vital role in determining the interaction between frame and body. The Young's modulus or modulus of elasticity is a ratio that defines the stiffness of a material under tensile stress. It is the ratio stress:strain. For a strip of rubber under a tensile pull we would expect it to be low, since the strain, the increase in length, would be high for a given stress in lb per square inch. For a length of high-tensile wire, such as piano wire, we would find the tensile modulus to be high.

For steel the value is 30×10^6 lb/in^2, for a typical aluminium alloy 10×10^6 lb/in^2 and for a typical glass-fibre reinforced plastic (GRP) as used in what we loosely call a fibreglass body the value can be as low as 1.0×10^6 lb/in^2.

To illustrate the importance of the elastic modulus let us consider a simple structural member such as a cantilevered beam as shown in Fig 8.1. For a certain deflection to occur (say, a movement of one-hundredth of an inch at the tip of

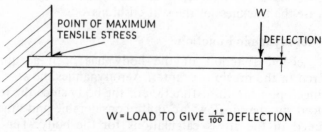

Fig 8.1   Cantilever beam.

the beam) the load required if the beam were made of steel would be three times that for an aluminium beam and thirty times that for a typical GRP beam.

The amount of load-sharing between the frame and the body depends to a great extent on the relative moduli of the materials. When a GRP body is mated to a steel frame the stresses are largely confined to the frame. When both frame and body are in the same materials the stresses are shared proportionately. It is perhaps fortunate that the high modulus of a steel frame protects a GRP body from external stresses since many GRP mouldings made by the popular contact moulding technique have ultimate strengths in the range 10 000 to 25 000 lb/in^2 against 65 000 lb/in^2 for mild steel and twice that for some alloy steels. For a rivetted aluminium alloy body shell mounted rigidly on a frame fabricated from aluminium alloy tubing the stiffness of the combination, as a first approximation, could be taken as additive. With a frame having a torsional stiffness of 8000 lb-ft per degree and a body with a value of 3000 lb-ft per degree the combined torsional resistance would be in the region of 10 000 lb-ft per degree.

MATERIALS

Metals

Mild Steel
The motor industry has a wealth of experience in the fabrication of frames and bodies in steel. It is a predictable reliable material and, its chief disadvantage, its poor resistance to corrosion, need not concern the builder of prototype sports cars which are not required to be driven on salted roads or even to survive for many years. Fabrication on a small scale is usually carried out by brazing or spot-welding sub-assemblies and completing the final assembly by welding these smaller sections together when placed on a plate jig. Furnace-brazing can be used for the smaller sub-assemblies, and spot-welding for the larger parts.

Aluminium Alloy

To avoid problems of heat-treatment, welding is usually avoided in the case of the duralumin-type alloys. The box-sections of the latest Bobsy frame (shown in Fig 8.2), a new American sports car for the SCCA's C Sports/racing class, are assembled by means of pop rivets of the type used in the aircraft industry. This semi-monocoque frame has a measured torsional resistance of 12 000 lb-ft per degree, a very high value for a short wheelbase car. The bodies designed by Alan Mann to race as Prototype Ford GT40s in 1966 at Le Mans were fabricated in a similar manner from aluminium alloy sheet and weighed 170 lb less than the production GT40 bodies made from GRP.

Magnesium Alloy

Magnesium is such a light metal that many will ask why it has not displaced all other materials for applications where lightness is at a premium. Remembering the early experi-

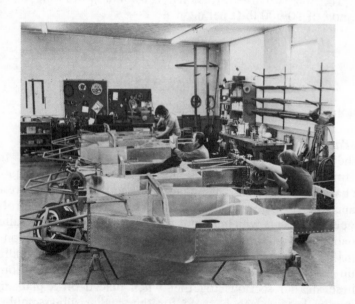

Fig 8.2   The Bobsy semi-monocoque frame.

ments, forty years ago when the author was still a student, he must admit to a certain prejudice since the early experiments which involved heat-treatment of large castings suffered setbacks after several serious explosions. Modern techniques have removed this danger during manufacture. The danger of fire and explosion still remains if the alloy is subjected to a high enough temperature. The Mercedes-Benz 300SLR which collided with an Austin Healey at Le Mans in 1955 and crashed into the crowd had its fuel tank burst into flames. Subsequent outbursts of a more explosive nature were thought to be caused by magnesium alloy which had been used as castings in the engine and transmission and in much lighter sections in the construction of the body. Contact with water (from a burst radiator, for example) will cause burning magnesium to explode.

Magnesium alloys then are only a low fire risk when used in very thick sections. One cannot make hard and fast rules, but sections with wall thicknesses below one-eighth inch should be avoided.

The density of magnesium alloy is about 1.8, against 2.8 for an aluminium alloy and 7.8 for mild steel. Its popularity for racing wheels is therefore easily understood. It has a second disadvantage, a poor resistance to corrosion, and this has been a problem for scrutineers in recent years. Aluminium forms a protective oxide layer in normal atmospheric conditions. Magnesium is not only as susceptible to corrosion as steel, but its strength is much more seriously impaired by the presence of cracks or notches, which can easily be formed when a corroded area has begun to spread inwards. The use of tyre levers can even start a corrosion crack if their use damages the protective paint. Steel particles from the levers deposited on the bare alloy will accelerate corrosion by electrolytic action. British Specification DTD 911 describes a method of protecting magnesium alloy surfaces by the use of a chromate primer and a resin-based paint.

Unlike steel which has an infinite fatigue life if the stresses are kept below a certain critical level, both magnesium and aluminium alloys have a limited fatigue life. This again creates a problem when either of these light alloys are used indiscriminately. The majority of cast wheels made today have cast-in date figures to identify the date of manufacture. This will be of value to scrutineers in the future, but no firm age-limit has yet been specified by the F.I.A. for alloy wheels.

Despite these limitations magnesium alloys are still very attractive, especially for large cast or forged components. The specific gravity is almost as low as that for GRP, yet the Young's modulus is much higher.

Plastics

Every enthusiastic motorist is aware of fibre-glass as a suitable material from which to mould car bodies in relatively low production quantities. In the Plastics Industry the general classification of this material is Glass Reinforced Plastics (GRP). It is made by impregnating spun glass fibre with a suitable thermo-setting resin. The glass fibre, being very strong, reinforces the weaker resin in the manner of the reinforcing bars in reinforced concrete.

The glass fibres are made by spinning, i.e. by extruding in a hot liquid state through a spinneret containing hundreds of fine holes. The continuous fibres are then wound up as cylindrical bobbins (cakes) and, after treatment with a chemical size to prepare the surface for bonding to the resin, the material is ready for use in the various moulding techniques.

Contact moulding is used for low volume production (less than 500 units per week). A simple mould, usually of GRP itself, is used and after application of a release agent and a thin coating of resin the first layer of fibre glass material, tailored to size, is laid by hand inside the mould. The first layer is always a smooth woven material to give a good outer surface finish. Popular practice is to use mats of fibre-glass for the remaining layers until the required thickness has been built up. The usual mat is made from random long staple fibres. For a higher strength product, where cost is not the first concern, layers of woven fabric are used throughout the section. The first layer is sprayed with resin until soaked, then pressed by a roller to consolidate it and remove air bubbles. More layers of mat or cloth are added, then more resin until the required thickness is reached. The tensile strength when cloth is used is at least twice that achieved with mat.

CFRP

High modulus carbon fibre is a recent development that holds great promise for the lightweight sports car of the future. The process was developed at the Royal Aircraft Establishment, Farnborough, and is now being made under licence by several British Companies. One of these is the Industrial Textile Division of Fothergill and Harvey Ltd of Littleborough, Lancashire, another is Courtaulds Ltd of Coventry who market it under the Trade Name of 'Grafil'. CFRP is the result of an intensive search for a completely new material with a higher stiffness to weight ratio than is available from any other engineering materials.

Carbon fibres are produced by carbonising filaments of polyacrilonitrile. The process is very costly and the cost of the actual fibres in the cheapest form of short staple or in flock form is about £20 per lb ($50 per lb). The most practical application today in the field of racing cars is in the form of pre-impregnated sheets, i.e. soaked in resin, and in this form it can be used to strengthen a GRP body in the areas that need to be stiffened. The original Ford GT40 bodies were not only heavy, but were not strong enough to withstand the battering imposed by two or three long-distance races. At an additional cost of about £300 ($750) 'pre-preg' sheets of CFRP were incorporated in the 1968 bodies. The weight of the body was reduced by about 100 lb and the body was found to be more durable, needing less patching between races and, in some cases remaining in serviceable condition for two complete seasons of racing.

There is little doubt that carbon fibre, used at first as a reinforcing material, and later in new forms and methods of application will be used much more widely in the future. Attempts to evolve less expensive methods of production are the subject of current research, but even using existing methods the snowballing influence of increasing demand will automatically reduce the cost. This phenomenon has already been seen in the case of titanium and its alloys, where the

increasing demands of the aircraft industry have already
started to cut prices.

A Comparison of Material Properties

By what seems to a simple automobile engineer a strange
coincidence, the *specific* modulus in tension, i.e. the Young's
modulus divided by the material density is almost identical
for steel, aluminium, magnesium and titanium and also for
their alloys. Table 8.1 serves to illustrate this and to show
that the *specific* tensile strength of a typical high-tensile alloy
steel, an aluminium alloy and a magnesium alloy are almost
the same.

The values given in this table could be misleading to the
layman. To illustrate how an engineer can use light alloys and
plastic materials to their best advantage it will be necessary to
become involved (but only to a small extent!) in a little
Strength of Materials theory.

Moments of Inertia

Any structural member of regular cross-section that is
subjected to certain loads will not be stressed to the same
extent at all points along its length or depth and the engineer
chooses a particular cross-section to make the most economical use of his materials. A typical H-section girder for
example places as much material as possible where it is more
effective in resisting bending. The web of the girder only
serves to locate the flanges as far as possible away from the
girder centre-line. The moment of inertia, or second moment
of area, as it is called in certain mathematical textbooks, of a
section has a profound influence on the strength of the
member.

Simple Bending Moments

Let us illustrate the part played by the Moment of Inertia by
the simple example of a rectangular section beam of width B
and depth A loaded by a central vertical load W and freely
supported at its ends so that it resists bending over a span L.
For simplicity let us neglect the weight of the beam itself.
The maximum bending moment is exerted at the centre
section and is equal to $1/4\ WL$. The maximum stress imposed

TABLE 8.1

Material	Density d g/ml	Tensile Strength S lb/in^2	Young's Modulus of Elasticity in Tension E lb/in^2	Specific Strength $\dfrac{S}{d}$	Specific Modulus (tension) $\dfrac{E}{d}$
METALS					
Mild Steel	7.8	65×10^3	30×10^6	8.3×10^3	3.8×10^6
80 Ton Alloy Steel, S99	7.8	180×10^3	30×10^6	23×10^3	3.8×10^6
Aluminium alloy, L65	2.8	67×10^3	10.5×10^6	24×10^3	3.7×10^6
Titanium alloy, DTD 5173	4.5	135×10^3	16.0×10^6	30×10^3	3.5×10^6
Magnesium alloy DTD 626A	1.8	40×10^3	6.4×10^6	22×10^3	3.6×10^6
PLASTICS					
GRP, low strength mat	1.4–1.6	$10-25 \times 10^3$	$0.8-1.8 \times 10^6$	$7-16 \times 10^3$	$0.6-1.1 \times 10^6$
GRP, high strength fabric	1.6–1.9	$35-60 \times 10^3$	$2.0-3.5 \times 10^6$	$22-30 \times 10^3$	$1.2-1.9 \times 10^6$
CFRP, 'Grafil' HM-S	1.60	150×10^3	27.4×10^6	94×10^3	17.1×10^6
CFRP, 'Grafil', HT-S	1.45	190×10^3	18.5×10^6	130×10^3	12.8×10^6

on the crystal-structure (or fibres) in the centre-section will occur at the furthest point from the neutral axis of the beam (the horizontal plane at which zero stress occurs), in this case the centre-line XX'.

At any point along the beam the stress is given by the following formula (which the student will find in any book on Strength of Materials):—

$$f = \frac{M \; c_x}{I}$$

where f is the stress in lb/in² ; M is the bending moment in lb-inches; c_x is the distance from the neutral axis, inches; I is the moment of inertia of the section, for which the units are in⁴ , as will be seen below.

The moment of inertia of a section is obtained by integrating the summation of each tiny area of the cross-section times the *square* of the distance of that tiny area from the neutral axis. As an example, for a tube the value of I is $\pi/64(D^4 - d^4)$. A 1 inch diameter tube with a wall thickness of 1/16 inch will have the same moment of inertia as a solid bar of about 0.8 inch diameter. The weight of the tube per foot run will be about 37 per cent of the weight of the solid section. By the same reasoning when using a rectangular bar to resist bending we place the longer side of the bar in the plane of the bending moment to obtain the maximum value of I. The diagram (Fig 8.3) shows our chosen

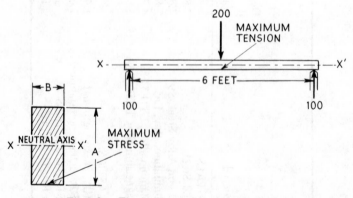

Fig 8.3   The beam used in the calculations.

TABLE 8.2

Material	Dimensions of Rectangular Section A x B inches	Weight lb per ft	Maximum Stress (at centre of 6 ft beam under 200 lb load) lb/in²	Deflection at Centre inches
METALS				
Mild Steel	1 3/4 x 5/8	3.7	11 300	0.019
80 Ton Alloy steel, S99	1 3/8 x 3/8	1.75	30 500	0.064
Aluminium alloy, L 65	1 3/4 x 5/8	1.33	11 300	0.054
Titanium alloy, DTD 5173	1 3/8 x 7/16	1.17	26,000	0.101
Magnesium alloy, DTD 626A	2 1/8 x 5/8	1.05	7 600	0.049
PLASTICS				
GRP, low strength mat	3 1/4 x 1	2.0	2 050	0.068
GRP, high strength fabric	2 1/8 x 5/8	1.08	7 600	0.088
CFRP, 'Grafil', HM-S	1 3/8 x 7/16	0.43	26 000	0.060
CFRP, 'Grafil', HT-S	1 3/8 x 3/8	0.33	30 500	0.104

example of a beam loaded by a 200 lb weight at the centre of a 6 ft span. The moment of inertia of the bar section, $I = 1/12\ A^3 B$ and the maximum tensile stress, which occurs in the fibres of the material on the lower face of the centre section, is:—

$$f_{max} = \frac{M\ A/2}{I}$$

$$= \frac{3600 \times A/2}{A^3\ B/12}$$

$$= \frac{21600}{A^2\ B}$$

We can now see how to gain from the lower densities of such materials as magnesium and GRP. Since the stress varies inversely as the square of the bar depth, a bar of twice the depth will cut the maximum stress to a quarter. Table 8.2 has been compiled to show how different materials compare on this basis. Maximum stresses in each case have been kept within the usual acceptable working limits. The superiority of Grafil over all the other materials on a strength per unit weight basis is remarkable. Where stiffness is critical, as for example, in a suspension link, a change from titanium to Grafil HM-S would reduce the weight by about 60 per cent and the link would suffer less deflection under load. Today the techniques of manufacture of carbon fibre plastics are still under development and the cost is very high, but the writer will be very surprised if we do not see some components on the highly stressed sections of the suspension system, frame and body of racing sports cars changed to this new material in the next five years.

CHAPTER NINE
The Basic Decisions in Engine Design

Lord Beeching, in a recent interview to 'The Sunday Times' spoke of the difficulty many of us have in identifying our basic problem. 'Most people', he said, 'don't do that because they can't get past the belt of fog which obscures the starting point'.

So, before we start making decisions about so vital a component as the power unit, let us attempt to define the problem. Once we know the problem we can start to face up to a few decisions.

THE BASIC PROBLEM

The power of the engine is probably the greatest single factor that counts, remembering all the time what Roger Penske once said: 'To finish first, first you have to finish'. The engine then must strike the right balance between power output and reliability; between power output per litre and between power output and weight. The designer who can provide an engine that is smaller, lighter and more powerful than the opposition and that lasts the distance need never worry about unemployment. If, however, he is completely conventional in his approach to design, his task is very difficult indeed, since the successful racing car designers who have set these conventions are among the finest engineers in the world.

THE BASIC DECISIONS

We now propose to consider some of the basic decisions that designers of racing engines have had to take in the past and the new decisions they face when new engineering developments appear on the horizon. Not all designers follow the same path and by the same token many engineers writing this chapter would no doubt arrive at a different set of conclusions. The decisions that concern us in this chapter are not minor. We are not concerned with detail design, such as the choice of camshaft drive or the position of the water pump. These are the $64 000 questions that keep designers awake at night. For example, why do we see so few turbocharged engines in European motor racing, while they reign supreme at Indianapolis? Why do the Porsche Company always choose air-cooling when all their rivals use liquid–cooled engines? Whatever happened to those fabulous two-strokes that such well-known engineers as Peter Berthon and Phil Irving predicted would power the Grand Prix cars of the Sixties? Should we be turning our thoughts to the Wankel engine as a possible challenge to the piston engine? These are some of the questions and in all fairness it would need a ten volume opus with about a dozen expert contributors to cover the subject in depth.

The Two-Stroke Cycle

Let us start with that fundamental decision between the two-stroke cycle and the four-stroke cycle that has haunted designers since the birth of the industry. In 1862 Beau de Rochas patented the four-stroke cycle and this was the cycle used by Otto for his gas engine and by all the early petrol driven horseless carriages. It is of course the conventional four-cycle principle that is used in our passenger vehicles today. Saab, were the noteworthy exception until recently, when they were forced to abandon the two-stroke principle to meet the American anti-pollution laws.

The very idea of an engine in which only one stroke in every four performs useful work must have seemed a sinful extravagance to an engineer with a careful Scottish upbringing. It was therefore natural that Glasgow engineer, Mr (later Sir) Dugald Clerk, should be the first to design run and patent in 1881 an engine operating on a two-stroke cycle. This early engine used a separate 'displacer' piston and cylinder to do the work of the missing strokes and can therefore be regarded as the forerunner of the supercharged two-strokes which are now used in large Marine Diesel engines and in some heavy commercial vehicles. The crankcase compression two-stroke was first made by Day in 1891.

The working principle, shown in Fig. 9.1, is seen to be that used in the popular work-horse two-stroke engines we use to drive our lawn mowers, power saws and motor scooters.

In the world of motor-cycle racing the success of the unsupercharged two-stroke engine has been phenomenal. Racing two-strokes can develop as much as 55 b.h.p. from a twin-cylinder 250 c.c. engine and 75 b.h.p. from a 500 c.c. single-cylinder engine. Notable examples are the Suzaki, the Yamaha and the Kawasaki from Japan, the MZ from East Germany and the Ossa from Spain. The working cycle of a

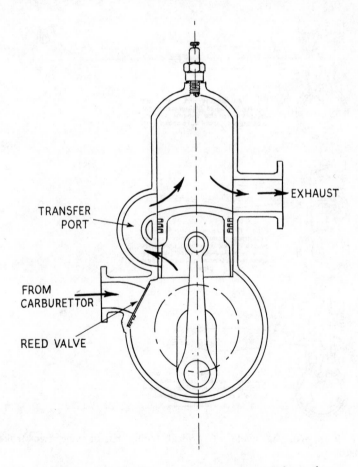

TRANSFER
PORT

EXHAUST

FROM
CARBURETTOR

REED VALVE

Fig 9.1   The crankcase compression two-stroke cycle.

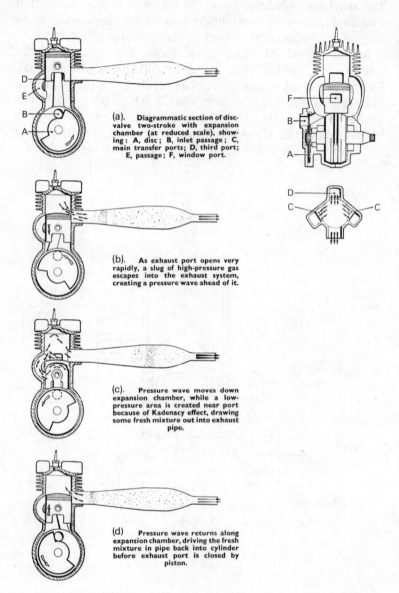

(a).   Diagrammatic section of disc-valve two-stroke with expansion chamber (at reduced scale), showing: A, disc; B, inlet passage; C, main transfer ports; D, third port; E, passage; F, window port.

(b).   As exhaust port opens very rapidly, a slug of high-pressure gas escapes into the exhaust system, creating a pressure wave ahead of it.

(c).   Pressure wave moves down expansion chamber, while a low-pressure area is created near port because of Kadenacy effect, drawing some fresh mixture out into exhaust pipe.

(d)   Pressure wave returns along expansion chamber, driving the fresh mixture in pipe back into cylinder before exhaust port is closed by piston.

Fig 9.2   Working cycle of typical racing motor-cycle two-stroke engine.

typical racing motor cycle two-stroke is illustrated in Fig 9.2. In this example the crankcase inlet port is controlled by a thin disc valve which is attached to the crankshaft. This is sometimes called a Zimmerman valve after the inventor. The use of a large expansion chamber, correctly shaped and sized, and placed as close as possible to the exhaust ports was first investigated and patented by Michael Kadenacy when developing high-speed two-stroke Diesel engines nearly forty years ago. The technique has been perfected in the last twenty years and is explained in simple terms in Fig 9.2. To prevent confusion we must explain that the technique differs from that used when 'ramming pipes' or tuned lengths are used on four-stroke engines. In the four-stroke technique the pipe length is chosen which gives a negative pulse in the exhaust port at the time of exhaust valve closing (see the author's earlier work, 'The Sports Car — its Design and Performance' for a description of the four-stroke technique).

Besides the introduction of the disc valve to control the intake timing to the crankcase, the efficiency of the crankcase as a compressor has been gradually improved since the days when the Scott Motor-Cycle Company first realized that the internal volume of the crankcase could be reduced dramatically by using circular crankshaft webs that were only slightly smaller in diameter than the space in which they rotated.

The use of Kadency expansion chambers is confined to constant speed engines or to racing engines operating over a very narrow speed range. For a true variable speed engine it is a mixed blessing. At the designed speed it gives a most impressive boost to the power curve, while at some other speed it introduces an embarassing hollow that is death to acceleration. A typical power curve is given in Fig 9.3. This curve is given by a racing two-stroke with a peak power output of 28 b.h.p. from a single 125 c.c. cylinder (224 b.h.p. per litre), an impressive output by any standards. To keep inside the working range of 11 000 to 12 500 rev/min it would be necessary to provide an 8-speed gearbox. This is quite normal for racing two-strokes and as many as 12 speeds have actually been used in motor-cycle racing.

The rotating parts in a motor-cycle engine, clutch and

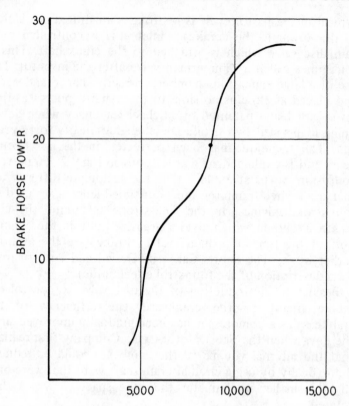

Fig 9.3   224 bhp per litre from a 125 cc racing two-stroke.

gearbox have such a low inertia that the time lost in making a succession of gearchanges before and after every corner is almost negligible. If however we were to step up the engine size to 3, 4 or even 5 litres, it would be necessary to provide an automatic transmission giving almost constant speed to make such a narrow speed range practicable.

Let us suppose, however, that a light reliable automatic transmission can be designed which will operate over this narrow speed range; what cylinder and crankshaft configuration would we use and how many cylinders would be required for a 3-litre engine to give comparable specific power outputs to the small racing motor-cycle engines? The highest specific powers are given by the smallest cylinders, but the boldest of designers would be daunted by the thought of a 3-litre engine with 24 cylinders each of 125 c.c. capacity. If we confine our comparison between engines of different sizes to ones with the same stroke/bore ratio we can state with fair accuracy that the power varies as the piston area.

Thus the specific power,

$$\text{b.h.p. per litre} = \frac{P}{d}$$

where P is a constant for engines sharing common design features. A higher value of P would be used, for example, for engines having twin OHC and multiple carburettors than for push-rod OHV touring engines.

For a racing motor-cycle two-stroke a suitable value of P would be 12 000, if d, the bore size is expressed in millimetres. Thus a 'square' series of such engines would be expected to yield the following specific powers.

TABLE 9.1
Variation of Specific Power with Bore
(Racing two-strokes of equal bore and stroke)

Bore and Stroke mm	Capacity c.c.	Specific Power b.h.p. per litre
54.15	125	221
68.2	250	176
86.0	500	140

One promising layout for a 3-litre two-stroke engine would be a 12-cylinder V with twin crankshafts geared together as shown in the sketch of Fig 9.4. This scheme was suggested by Phil Irving. The geared crank arrangement proved the undoing of the H-16 engine in the Formula 1 BRM, but one must accept some compromise of this kind if we are to provide separate compartments for each cylinder with no interconnection between banks. Fuel injection into the inlet ports would fit admirably into this layout, but the

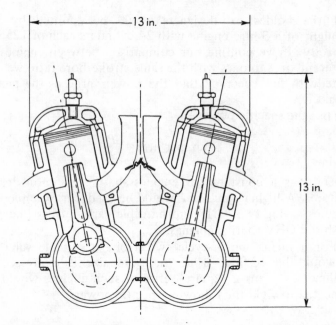

Fig 9.4   Proposal by Phil Irving, M.I.Mech E., MSAE, for a 3-litre
V-12 of 68mm bore and stroke.

provision of large enough Kadenacy-type expansion chambers
would present a problem, as indicated in Fig 9.5. It would
almost certainly call for a compromise since the ports would
be too close to permit the use of full-size expansion

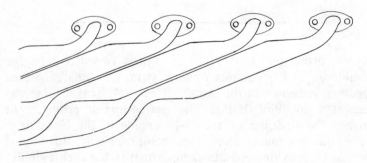

Fig 9.5   Stacked 'Kadenacy' expansion chambers on a multi-cylinder
two-stroke.

chambers. Making an allowance for this factor we could predict an output of no more than 150 b.h.p. per litre from such an engine. Simple crank-operated disc valves would be difficult to use on an in-line engine, but a rotary valve system could be driven by a common shaft or skirt controlled ports could be used as indicated in Fig 9.4, although such engines do not usually achieve the same specific outputs as disc-valve racing engines.

Comparing this specific output with that of current racing four-stroke engines we find an almost identical value. The Series 12 Formula 1 Cosworth DFV engine is giving a very reliable 147 b.h.p. per litre, the BRM V-12 is giving close to 150 b.h.p. per litre and the flat-12 Ferrari is reputed to give slightly more in Formula 1 tune, about 160 b.h.p. per litre. The Cosworth engine has a usable speed range of 7000 to 10 500 rev/min. No driver would consider swapping this flexibility for the peaky power curve of a typical racing two-stroke.

On the above basis then there is no promise of greater power from the adoption of the principles used to make the small racing two-strokes so successful in their particular field. They do offer the advantage of simplicity and, if we can extract the target power output without recourse to liquid cooling, there would be a second advantage of reduced weight.

Let us consider the known disadvantages.

1. The cylinder barrels in a two-stroke have hot exhaust ports on one side and cool transfer ports on the other. This has always created gas sealing problems since the bore tends to distort as the engine reaches operating temperature. It is inevitable also that the pistons will run hotter in a two-stroke since they lack the cooling action of a full stroke devoted to the inspiration of a fresh relatively cool charge. Larger piston clearances are used in a two-stroke to combat these twin evils, but the danger of piston failure from gas leakage in the exhaust port zone is always present. Piston seizure on a two-stroke has always been the most frequent cause of retirement. The use of low-expansion silicon-aluminium alloys has helped in recent years, but a more effective cure is the adoption of

liquid cooling instead of the more popular air-cooling since the ports can be well cooled by a fast flow of water around the port bridges. Unfortunately the two-stroke loses its advantage of lightness with the change.

2. The exhaust system on a multi-cylinder two-stroke would be very bulky. For a cylinder of 250 c.c. the correct expansion chamber must be about 6 inches in diameter (or the equivalent cross-sectional area) at the widest point. Not only would it be difficult to find room to accommodate such a collection of chambers (six per side on Phil Irving's V-12 design) in the confined space outside a mid-engined sports car, but the weight, even when frabricated from titanium, would reduce the potential weight savings envisaged by the supporters of the two-stroke to a marginal level.

3. A racing two-stroke is very wasteful in fuel; even more extravagant than a racing four-stroke with large valve overlap. The description of the working cycle given in Fig 9.2 was an oversimplification. Mixing of the fresh charge with the exhaust gases is inevitable. One could hardly hope to keep the layers stratified at such high gas velocities. To scavenge the cylinder effectively and to extract racing power outputs from this small cylinder it is necessary to allow large quantities of fresh mixture to pass out through the exhaust ports. At the designed speed the Kadenacy effect returns a portion of this fresh gas back into the cylinder, but to be sure that this contains only a small percentage of exhaust gas it is necessary for the gas further down the pipe to carry to waste large quantities of fresh mixture. There is so much petrol air mixture in the exhaust system of a racing motor-cycle that a hot-spot in any part of it will sometimes trigger off an explosion that rips open the entire chamber.

A competition sports car using a multi-cylinder version of the racing two-stroke would have a fuel consumption under racing conditions about 25 per cent higher than the present engines. This would be a serious handicap since the car would have to carry 25 per cent more fuel or make more pit stops for re-fuelling.

The use of direct fuel injection would of course give a more economical two-stroke. By scavenging the exhaust gases by means of air only no fuel would be lost in the exhaust system and the pressure-pulse charging effect of the Kadenacy expansion box would still take place. Fuel would be injected right into the combustion chamber as in a diesel engine. Unlike the diesel however, the fuel would be injected during the compression stroke immediately after the exhaust ports had been covered but early enough in the compression stroke to allow the fuel to become well mixed with the air before the spark occurred. This at first sight appears to be a perfect solution to the wasteful behaviour of the racing two-stroke. Unfortunately it throws away about 10 per cent of the power in doing this and power, it will be remembered, *reliable power* was the basic problem we established on the first page of the chapter. By using air to scavenge the exhaust gases instead of mixture we lose all the benefits of evaporative cooling. The droplets of petrol that enter the crankcase help to lower the temperature of the charge, thus helping the engine to induce a larger mass of air at each induction stroke. Fuel that is still unevaporated after the transfer ports are uncovered continues to evaporate during the transfer process, again helping to lower the temperatures of the charge that is eventually captured by the cylinder when the transfer port is closed. A loss of about 10 per cent in power cannot be countenanced, not even to improve economy. Port injection is therefore the only solution.

Summarizing all the above, we can say that there is very little to choose in their current stages of development between the two types of engine in their own spheres. Since the development of an 8 or 12, or even 16-cylinder two-stroke would present many problems and would be a very expensive project it is most unlikely that any manufacturer of sports cars will even consider such a step in the near future. One cannot predict the behaviour of eccentric millionaires but it is almost a certainty that the Air Pollution Research Advisory Committee in the USA is unlikely to encourage the development of two-stroke engines. Neither will our own Noise Abatement Society!

The Cooling Media

The majority of high performance automobile racing engines are liquid-cooled and if the decision went by majority rule the Porsche Company would be put out of business. Ferry Porsche and his active little sports car business, however, are alive and well and living in Stuttgart, and their air-cooled engines are not only highly competitive, but their whole range of production sports cars are highly desirable. What then are the advantages and disadvantages of the two systems?

The specific heat of air (its capacity to absorb heat) is much lower than that of water. On a mass-flow basis an air flow of 4 lb per minute will be required to remove as much heat as a water flow of 1 lb per minute. On a volume basis the difference in flow rates becomes about 4000 to 1. On the other hand this large throughput of air only involves the size of the cooling fan required and the dimensions of the ducting to pass it around the cylinders and over the cylinder heads. The air itself adds nothing to the weight of the engine installation. With a water-cooled engine or one cooled by a water–ethylene glycol mixture we must carry on the car all the coolant contained in the head and cylinder water jackets, in the header tank and in the radiators and all the attendant piping. In addition there is the weight of the radiators and water pump (sometimes a cooling fan). The weight of the ducting and cooling fan used on an air-cooled engine is much lighter by comparison. As a rough guide on an engine capacity basis we can say that a saving of about 30 lb per litre is made by using air cooling, with a proportionately smaller saving for engines above 3 litres.

Air cooling imposes certain design limitations. One of these is that the cylinder centres on an in-line engine cannot be as closely spaced as on a liquid-cooled engine. Most of the heat is transferred to the cooling air through the cylinder heads. Even with the inter-fin spacing at the recommended minimum of 0.10 inches (see 'Air Cooling of Automobile Engines' by J. Mackerle, ME, paper to Institution of Mechanical Engineers, 1961) the problem of providing sufficient area of finning around the cylinder heads and at the top end of the cylinder barrels calls for a cylinder spacing of no less than 1.4 D, where D is the bore size. This distance makes the in-line layout far too long and bulky for a racing type of air-cooled engine. For a 3-litre engine it would give an overall length about 8 inches longer than the corresponding liquid-cooled engine. Apart from the additional space to be provided in the frame an increase in length of as much as 8 inches in the crankshaft can reduce the frequency of the natural torsional vibrations of the crankshaft until they resonate with the firing frequency. To avoid this calls for a stiffer and heavier crankshaft.

So, by the laws of natural selection, we find that successful multi-cylinder air-cooled engines are of the opposed-piston (flat) type as in the Porsche engines or of the V configuration. It is of interest that the 3.7-litre Steyr air-cooled engine which Sydney Allard used so successfully in his Hill Climb Special was a V-8. When two big-end bearings share the same crank-pin this in itself establishes a wider cylinder spacing than is used on an in-line engine. Cylinder centres on the two banks are, of course, offset but this adds very little to the overall length of the engine. This is why the early success of the flat-4 Porsches was followed by even more successful 6s and 8s and finally a 12, all essentially to the same basic design.

Nevertheless the design of a high-output air-cooled engine is no easy matter. The author's war-time experience of the problems associated with the Bristol air-cooled aero engines made him a little envious of the development engineers working on the Rolls-Royce Merlin engine, where the sound insulating properties of the water-jackets muffled so much of the sound and fury that was happening in the combustion chambers. One problem is the provision of a well distributed area of cooling fins over a cylinder head which has a relatively cool inlet port on one side and a very hot exhaust port on the other. There must always be a tendency to distort the top end of the cylinder barrel from this eccentric heat flow. The extent of the finning on the Porsche Type 917 can be seen from Fig 9.6.

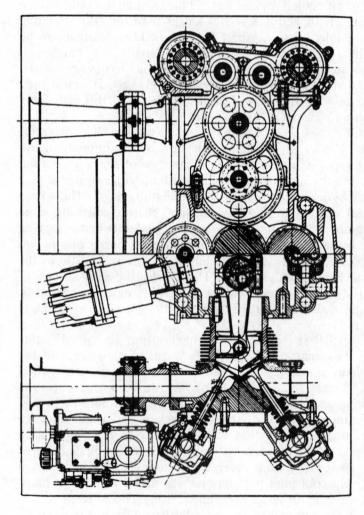

Fig 9.6 Porsche 917 engine—a two-plane cross-section. Note cylinder head design.

The advantages and disadvantages of air-cooling are listed below:

Advantages
1. Low weight.
2. Reduced vulnerability to damage by minor shunts or other minor accidents (fan, fan belt and ducting less vulnerable than exposed radiators).
3. No loss of reliability from internal or external water leaks.

Disadvantages
1. Higher internal operating temperatures at the same specific power output (i.e. higher surface temperatures inside the combustion chamber, on the piston crown and the exhaust valve seats).
2. Mechanically noisier.

Since we are not concerned about noise in a racing sports car there is only one real disadvantage, but that is not one to be dismissed lightly. The temperature in the region of the exhaust valve seat under full-load conditions is well recognized as a serious threat to reliability in air-cooled engines. For reliable operation of an exhaust valve, even with sodium cooling, the centre of the valve head should not exceed 750°C (1385°F) for long periods. Heat can only flow out of the exhaust valve by way of the seat (with which it is in contact for about two-thirds of the time) and to a limited extent along the stem and through the valve guide. Since the cylinder head material reaches a higher temperature in the region of the exhaust ports in an air-cooled engine (about 40–50°C higher) than it does in a liquid-cooled engine there is every reason for the valve itself to run at a higher temperature on full-load. The piston crown also has a tendency to reach higher temperatures than in a corresponding liquid-cooled engine and this could again be a potential source of engine failure in large bore engines. The use of an aluminium alloy for both head and barrel is now common practice and to provide a compatible running surface for the pistons and rings Porsche deposit a layer of hard chrome. Since aluminium alloy is a much superior conductor of heat the cylinder walls on the latest Porsche engines will run at a lower temperature than the older engines with cast-iron cylinder barrels. There are other methods available today to make it possible to use aluminium for the cylinder bores. The cylinder blocks for the General Motors Vega are now die-cast in a high-silicon (16–18%) aluminium alloy. To improve oil retention the rubbing surface is etched and the rubbing surfaces of the pistons are given a light plating of iron. To assist the initial bedding-in and to prevent rust formation in storage a final deposit of tin is given to the pistons.

Porsche versus The Rest

Since Porsche won the World Championship for Prototype Sports Cars in 1971 they have not competed as a Works' sponsored team. To make a direct comparison it is therefore necessary to compare the engines used during the three consecutive years 1969–71. Out of 31 races in this period Porsche won 24 times, Alfa Romeo won three times, Ford won twice and Ferrari and Lola once each.

As we will discuss at length in the next chapter the specific power developed by an engine is influenced to a remarkable extent by the number of cylinders and by the stroke/bore ratio. The engine used in the Porsche 917 and the Ferrari 512S can, however, be compared without prejudice to either. They are both of 5 litres, capacity, both 12-cylinder engines and their bore and stroke are almost identical. They both have fuel injection and twin overhead camshaft valve operation and the only other important difference, besides of course the method of cooling, is that the Ferrari engine has four valves per cylinder, the Porsche only two. Below we give their specifications:

Ferrari 512S First appearance Daytona, 1970.
  12 cylinders in 60° V formation; 4994 c.c. capacity; bore 87 mm; stroke 70 mm; twin OHC with four valves per cylinder; Lucas fuel injection; 580 b.h.p. at 8500 rev/min (116 b.h.p. per litre).

Porsche 917 First appearance Brands Hatch, 1971.
  12 cylinders in flat (boxer) configuration; 4998 c.c. capacity; bore 86.8 mm; stroke 70.4 mm; twin OHC with

two valves per cylinder; Bosch fuel injection; 630 b.h.p. at 8300 rev/min (126 b.h.p. per litre).

If one makes an allowance for the difference of one year in the dates of introduction of the two engines there appears to be little to choose between air or water as the cooling medium on a basis of specific power. The Porsche engine, which used magnesium alloy to such an extent that nearly 30 per cent of its total weight came from these components, weighed 528 lb. The total weight of the Ferrari is not known, but when one remembers to include the radiators in this comparison, a fair guess would be 600–650 lb.

We can only conclude this section with the following comment. Design know-how is a valuable commodity; Porsche know how to design air-cooled engines, their rivals know how to design liquid-cooled engines. What profit would there be then in any of them changing when the resulting products are so close in performance?

Supercharging

Supercharging may be defined as the use of a compressor (blower or supercharger) to raise the induction pressure above normal atmospheric pressure. By charging the cylinders with an air/fuel mixture of greater density than is possible with a naturally aspirated engine more fuel can be burned during each working cycle and more power can be produced.

Supercharging has been out of favour in European racing circles for about twenty years. When the original 1.5-litre BRM with two-stage centrifugal superchargers challenged the 4.5-litre Ferraris (and was dogged by almost total unreliability from its extremely complex mechanism) the use of alcohol fuel was permitted by the rules of the period. The problems of cooling a supercharged engine without the tremendously increased evaporative cooling effects conferred by alcohol fuel are very real. Under the existing Formula 1 rules one would need to develop a specific power of 300 b.h.p. per litre to equal the current unsupercharged engines, or more realistically to allow for the higher fuel consumption of the supercharged engine, one would have to produce about 350 b.h.p. per litre.

Cars competing in Groups 1 to 5, however, have a much more reasonable 'equivalence formula' for supercharging. The rule is simple. A supercharged car has its actual cubic capacity multiplied by 1.4 and must enter in the class 'corresponding to the fictive volume thus obtained'. To compete against unsupercharged 3-litre Group 5 racing sports cars then the capacity of a supercharged engine would have to be limited to 2.14 litres. Let us examine the future prospects of the supercharged engine on this basis.

Mechanically-driven Superchargers

The vane-type supercharger is the most popular mechanically driven blower in use today. An eccentrically mounted rotor carries sliding vanes which contact the inner surface of the cylindrical blower casing. Mixture is trapped between pairs of blades as these pass the inlet port and, by the eccentric action of the rotor, the trapped pockets of mixture are compressed to the required induction pressure by the time the rotor has carried them round to the delivery port. This type of blower must be lubricated since the blades have a sliding action inside the rotor and a rubbing contact with the casing. A small amount of engine oil is usually metered to the blower for this purpose. A cross-section of a vane-type blower is shown in Fig 9.7.

Another popular type for direct-drive applications is the Roots blower. This is a form of gear pump in which pairs of rotors are geared together to rotate at the same speed in

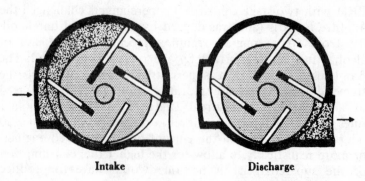

Intake   **Discharge**

Fig 9.7   Vane-type supercharger.

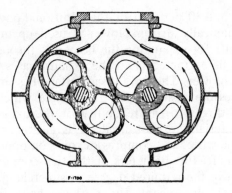

Fig 9.8   A Roots-type supercharger.

opposite directions. The rounded lobes of the rotors (usually two per rotor, but occasionally three) are shaped to maintain a small clearance at all times across the faces of the rotors and between each rotor and the end casings. A cross-section of a twin-lobe Roots blower is shown in Fig 9.8. The gears driving the two rotors are housed in a separate casing outside the compressor section of the blower and these gears can be splash-lubricated as in a normal gearbox. The rotors require no lubrication since there is no rubbing contact. With so many leakage paths the Roots blower is rather inefficient at low speeds, but at speeds above about 4000 rev/min the Roots blower is usually more efficient than the eccentric vane blower. The mixture is pumped in the spaces between the rotors and the casing, no compression taking place until the pocket of mixture comes into contact with the higher pressure gases on the delivery side.

Turbocharging
Turbocharging is a modern name for an old system in which the exhaust gases are expanded through the blades of a gas turbine, the turbine shaft being directly connected to the impellor of a centrifugal supercharger. As early as 1923 a Bristol biplane had an exhaust-driven supercharger fitted to its Jupiter III engine for high altitude experimental flights by the Royal Aircraft Establishment, Farnborough. The attraction of turbocharging lies in the overall efficiency of the

system. About 30 per cent of the additional power provided by a mechanically driven blower is used up in driving the blower itself. By expanding the hot gases through a turbine energy can be extracted from the exhaust gases to operate a centrifugal blower. The only disadvantage lies in the increased back-pressure upstream of the turbine which can sometimes be a threat to the reliability of the exhaust valves if suitable materials are not used. It is customary to mount both turbine wheel and compressor rotor on opposite ends of the same shaft, the diameters of the two components being chosen to give the required degree of supercharge for a given back-pressure. In recent times there have been several successful commercial applications of this principle, notably on large truck engines, and in 1961, after five years development work Chevrolet of America put into production the Corvair Monza Spyder and Oldsmobile (another General Motors product) introduced the Jetfire, two high-performance vehicles fitted with turbochargers.

On the Corvair the 11-bladed turbine disc was only 2.97 inches in diameter and the 14-bladed compressor rotor was 3.00 inches in diameter. The maximum speed reached by the two discs was 70 000 rev/min (yes, 70 not 7000!). The Oldsmobile used slightly smaller discs and the maximum speed was 90 000 rev/min. One of the problems with turbocharging which was only partially solved at this time was the time lag between the driver flooring the accelerator and the actual build-up of a high enough boost pressure to start the desired surge in power. The sequence of events will explain this. The opening of the throttle admitted more mixture to the cylinders (but only at the prevailing boost pressure); the burning of the increased supply of mixture generated a greater mass flow of exhaust gas which then accelerated the turbine from its relatively slow speed of, say, 20 000 rev/min to a higher speed; this in turn increased the boost pressure and the mixture entering the cylinders was now at a higher density; this increased the mass flow to the turbine again and the boost pressure rose to a higher level. To use an old simile it is like trying to lift yourself up by your bootstraps. The inertia of the two tiny rotors and their shaft is negligible and with a full boost available from the start the lag would only be about half a second. The time-lag on the Corvair was variously reported by the American Motoring Press as from 2 to 4 seconds. The Oldsmobile engineers were not happy with this and they designed a by-pass system which reduced the lag to about 1 second. The turbocharger was designed to give full boost at an engine speed of only 2200 rev/min. At higher engine speeds the surplus exhaust gas was by-passed to atmosphere. The Oldsmobile had a maximum exhaust back-pressure of 13 lb/in^2, while that on the Corvair rose to as much as 20.

Recent work in Europe has been in the research department of the BMW Company. Turbocharging has been applied to the 2002TI 2-litre engine which is fitted with the Kugelfischer fuel injection system which injects directly into the combustion chambers. Although the normal limiting engine speed is 7000 rev/min the maximum boost pressure of 14 lb/in^2 is reached at an engine speed of 4500 rev/min. The maximum turbine speed is 80 000 rev/min and the maximum exhaust back-pressure about 20 lb/in^2. Boost pressure is controlled to 14 lb/in^2 and as the engine speed increases above 4500 rev/min the surplus air is blown to waste. With direct fuel injection timed to occur after the inlet valve has closed only air is blown to waste, not mixture. Another advantage of this BMW system is the liberal use of air to cool the exhaust valves. A racing camshaft with a valve overlap of 120° is used. With boost pressures as high as 14 lb/in^2 large quantities of air flow past the exhaust valves during the overlap period, helping to keep the exhaust valves at a safe temperature and at the same time giving an excellent scavenging of the combustion chambers. This system is a much more economical way of keeping the exhaust valves cool than the traditional racing engine method of cooling the exhaust valves by allowing large amounts of mixture to escape during the overlap period. This sedate-looking little saloon has a genuine (DIN) power rating of 280 b.h.p. and has lapped the Spa circuit at 123 m.p.h.

The most impressive success story in the long saga of turbocharging has been the triumph of the turbocharged Fords and Offenhausers at Indianapolis. These engines are boosted by various competitors to 30 to 35 lb/in^2 and have

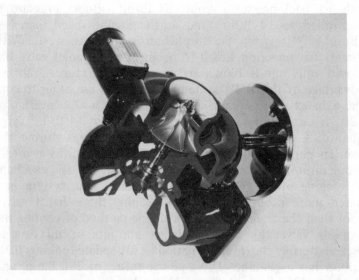

Fig 9.9   Turbocharger of the type manufactured by Holset Engineering Co Ltd. of Huddersfield, England and marketed world-wide by the Lucas Company. The exhaust turbine wheel is at the rear, exhausting downwards; the air delivery from the compressor to the induction manifold is at the top right.

shown dynamometer readings of as much as 850 b.h.p. from only 2.6 litre engine capacity (but only for a few seconds!). Maximum power on the track is usually limited to about 700 b.h.p. on the Offys and 725 b.h.p. on the Fords. The art of survival at Indianapolis with these engines has been well demonstrated as an inspired guess at the right boost pressure. In 1971 A. J. Foyt actually stopped at the pits on Lap 14 to have the maximum boost pressure on his Ford engine increased when he realized that he had underestimated the opposition. Despite this poor start he still finished in third position.

On the basis of a reliable 700 b.h.p. from 2.6 litres the turbocharged engine is still no challenge to the existing Formula 1 engines, but it does appear to be a likely contender in future Groups 4 and 5 sports car racing.

A 2.14-litre supercharged engine (by the current FIA multiplication factor of 1.4) could compete against 3-litre unsupercharged engines. If one allows about 10 per cent lower power than that used at Indianapolis to improve reliability in long distance sports car races, one could still anticipate about 520 b.h.p. from a 2.1-litre turbocharged racing engine and this is more than we can anticipate from 3-litre unsupercharged engines in the next four or five years. One would like to see some promise that the multiplication factor was not to be changed unfavourably before embarking on such a project.

Gas Turbines

Gas Turbines have been in regular use for heavy transport vehicles for several years. For passenger cars they have only been made in experimental quantities, notably by Chrysler and American Motors and the Rover Company in Great Britain. Rover, in conjunction with BRM built an experimental sports car which ran with commendable reliability at Le Mans in 1963 and 1965. The Ferguson-Novi 4WD gas turbine car which was entered by Andy Granatelli at Indianapolis in 1966 and 1967 came very close to winning this American Classic. It was, indeed, a decision to reduce the permitted turbine nozzle area by 35 per cent in future designs that discouraged Granatelli from continuing to compete with his obviously very successful turbine car.

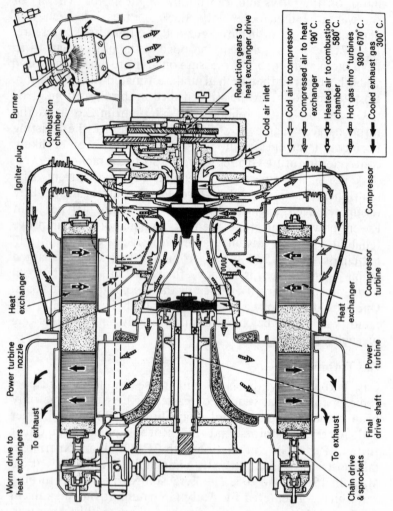

Reduction gears to heat exchanger drive

Cold air inlet

Compressor

⇨	Cold air to compressor
⇩	Compressed air to heat exchanger 190° C.
⇦	Heated air to combustion chamber 580° C.
⇨	Hot gas thro" turbines 930–670° C.
➡	Cooled exhaust gas 300° C.

Burner

Combustion chamber

Igniter plug

Heat exchanger

Power turbine nozzle

Worm drive to heat exchangers

To exhaust

Compressor turbine

Heat exchanger

Power turbine

Final drive shaft

Chain drive & sprockets

To exhaust

Fig 9.10   Simplified layout of Rover-BRM Le Mans gas turbine.

A typical gas-turbine engine is shown schematically in Fig 9.10. Air enters through an air filter and silencer (not shown) and is compressed by a radial or axial compressor with a pressure ratio of about 4 or 5 to 1. From the compressor the air is delivered via diffuser channels into the combustion chamber. It is customary to pass the air over the jacketted outside of the combustion chamber to impart additional heat to the intake air and help to keep the very hot walls of the chamber at a temperature that will prevent them from burning out. Combustion chambers differ in detail design, but the basic idea is to provide a primary combustion zone into which the fuel is sprayed continuously under pressure from a centrally placed burner. The spinning primary air mixes with the burning fuel droplets as they pass along the chamber to the zone where the secondary air is added to complete the combustion process. The hot gases are guided to set up a vortex flow to rotate the first turbine stage and the torque developed by this turbine is used to drive the compressor. The gases are then re-directed by variable nozzle blades to drive the power turbine. This is the turbine which is connected through a reduction gear to drive the output shaft.

For economical operation it is necessary to use regenerators to extract as much heat as possible from the gases. These regenerator discs are usually constructed from a special ceramic material with a high resistance to thermal shock. This material called 'Pyroceram' is made by the Corning Glass Company of America and in this application is constructed into a cylindrical matrix containing thousands of triangular cross-sectioned passages through which the hot gases are passed. Two regenerators are shown in Fig 9.10 and these are gear-driven to rotate very slowly. The heat which is stored in the surface layers of the matrices is given up to the airstream which passes in the reverse direction on the opposite side of each regenerator. This air, which is passing from the compressor towards the inlet of the combustion chamber, is raised in temperature by as much as 400°C (720°F) at full load by means of the regenerators. Before the development of regenerators the first Rover turbine car was notoriously extravagant in its fuel consumption. The RAC actually gave the overall consumption of the first Rover turbine car, Jet I, at 4 m.p.g. The Rover-BRM sports car, after competing at Le Mans in 1965 was road tested by 'Motor' and they gave the overall consumption of this car, fitted with regenerators, at 14.2 m.p.g.

The current F.I.A. formula to establish an 'equivalence' between reciprocating piston engines and gas turbines applies to all classes and groups. It is rather complex and is based on the total gas flow directed by the first stage stator blades or nozzles (the stationary blades or passages that direct the hot gases at the high pressure turbine) and the pressure ratio of the compressor driven by this turbine. This formula, based on extensive study by two turbine experts, Peter Spear and Noel Penny, is as follows:—

$$A = \frac{C \times 0.09625}{(3.10 \times R) - 7.63}$$

A is the permitted high pressure nozzle area, expressed in square centimetres. Where the nozzle blades are adjustable they are measured at the maximum opening.
C is the cylinder capacity of the reciprocating engine in the competing class, expressed in cubic centimetres.
R is the total pressure ratio of the compressor. This is obtained by multiplying together a value for each stage, defined as follows:—

for subsonic axial compressors	= 1.15 per stage
for trans-sonic axial compressors	= 1.15 per stage
for radial compressors	= 4.25 per stage

Thus a compressor with 1 radial and 4 axial subsonic stages will be designated as having a pressure ratio of:—

$$4.25 \times 1.15 \times 1.15 \times 1.15 \times 1.15 = 7.41$$

This formula can be revised after giving 12 months notice, such notice starting from the first day of January following the date on which the decision is taken.

The USAC, who control racing at Indianapolis, use a much more simple formula based on the annular flow to the compressor. In January 1967 the USAC Board ratified a formula which specified a maximum area for the compressor inlet of 23 in² for axial flow compressors and 28.5 for radial flow. Andy Granatelli, who had previously sponsored the spectacular, but unreliable, supercharged Novi-engined cars, turned his attentions in 1966 to the gas turbine and a 4WD Ferguson-Novi was developed, based on a P104 Ferguson chassis and an STN-6 Pratt and Whitney gas turbine, built by United Aircraft of Canada. The long in-line layout of an aircraft gas turbine is not ideal for automotive use and the engine had to be placed in tandem alongside the driver.

Torque from a gas turbine engine, is highest at minimum rev/min, an excellent characteristic it shares with the steam engine. On the STN-6 turbine the starting torque was 900 lb-ft. This fell gradually to about 500 lb-ft at a road speed of 190 m.p.h. For the 1968 Indianapolis 500 Granatelli joined forces with Lotus and the Lotus Type 56 Indianapolis car was converted into a gas-turbine car, the Type 56B. The permitted compressor inlet area had meanwhile been reduced by 35 per cent, some said in an attempt to 'hobble' the threat from the gas-turbine. Despite further development on the Pratt and Whitney turbine it was no longer competitive and the Indianapolis race has for the last four years been dominated by the turbocharged reciprocating engines.

The gas turbine suffers from pick-up lag, probably to a greater extent than the turbocharged piston engine. Pratt and Whitney claim to have reduced this lag from the region of 3–4 seconds that existed on the Indianapolis turbine in 1967 to as little as 1 second. The compressor turbine is now set to 'idle' at a minimum speed that is 60 per cent of maximum. Lift-off lag still remains as an embarrassment to the driver. Not only does he miss the engine braking effect that a piston engine gives, but the power remains on for a full second while he is braking into a corner. The technique used at Indianapolis was to brake earlier and open the throttle a second earlier than normal to come out of the turn.

Sam Williams, who designed the Williams Type WR-26 turbine which American Motors have installed in their Hornet car, has partially solved this problem by using a gas by-pass system to divert the gas flow from the power turbine when the accelerator is closed. This cuts off power immediately, but there is still no engine braking action. A free-wheel device fitted between the compressor shaft and the power turbine shaft serves a double purpose. Failure of a driveshaft or a universal joint at any point between the power turbine and the road wheels could result in catastrophic overspeeding of the power turbine. The Williams free-wheel prevents this since an overspeed of the power turbine that exceeds a fixed ratio of the compressor speed causes the two shafts to be locked together by the clutch mechanism. This same device can also be used to give engine braking when descending a hill. The AMC turbine car uses a Borg-Warner 3-speed automatic transmission, thus when descending a steep hill low gear can be engaged. This causes the power turbine to attempt to overspeed, which automatically locks the power turbine to the compressor and provides compression braking to retard the car.

Future of the Gas Turbine

Superficially the gas turbine as a racing car power unit seems to be in the doldrums. Behind the scenes, however, are developments which could change its prospects overnight. The thermal efficiency and power output of a gas turbine is limited by safe operating temperatures. Normal commercial gas turbines restrict the gas temperature in contact with the turbine blades to about 950°C (1740°F). Using the more expensive 'super alloys', as one would for racing, permits the gas exit the combustion chamber to be as high as 1050°C (1920°F). This is close to the present limit, but an increase of only 100°C (180°F) in this working temperature would increase power output by an estimated 17 per cent. Several companies are working on the development of high-temperature ceramics that would make even higher operating temperatures a reality. Advanced Material Engineering Ltd. (a consortium of British government research interests and private firms such as British Leyland, Clark-Chapman and Doulton) have a most promising material in silicon nitride, which can be moulded in powder form to produce a sintered product or, by mixing with a carrier material that can be flashed-off during firing, can be extruded through a die.

United Aircraft Research Laboratories are concentrating on the development of a very high speed single-stage radial compressor and have claimed to be able to operate at a speed of 136 000 rev/min to give a pressure ratio of 12 to 1 from this single stage. Under existing FIA rules a very light gas turbine could be made with such a compressor.

One can only speculate today, but the gas turbine as a racing car power unit is still liable to spring back into life when the new materials become commercially available.

Rotating Combustion Engines

In the seventeen years that have elapsed since Felix Wankel invented his rotating combustion engine the many licencees all over the world have been finding their various solutions to the problems that stood between them and commercial success. Satisfactory apex seals are now a reality in two or three forms, rotor and casing distortion has been brought under control and lubricating oil consumption is now reasonably low. In production today we see considerable numbers of the twin-rotor Mazda made in Japan and of the earlier design, also twin-rotor by NSU of Germany. The experimental C111 Mercedes sports car has been increased from a 3-rotor unit to a 4-rotor giving 350 b.h.p. at 7000 rev/min, but no plans for production have been announced.

The three-sided rotor of the Wankel engine is eccentrically mounted on the output shaft and geared to it through an internal gear and pinion to give a ratio of 3 to 1 (see Figs 9.11 and 9.12). For every revolution of the rotor the output shaft revolves three times. The geometric shape of the casing, called an *epitrochoid* was the subject of Wankel's original patent and is the locus of any one of the three apex seals. Rotary combustion engines with four, five or more sides to the rotor are possible and were covered in the original patent, but the three-sided design gives the most compact engine. Not only is it necessary to provide effective long-life seals at the three contact points of the rotor with the casing, but the sides of the rotor must also be sealed to prevent by-passing of the charge from one compartment to the next on the sides of the rotor. The engine is called a rotating combustion engine since the separate charges of gas trapped between the apex seals rotate in turn into the combustion zone and the gas moves tangentially across the fixed sparking plug. The engine

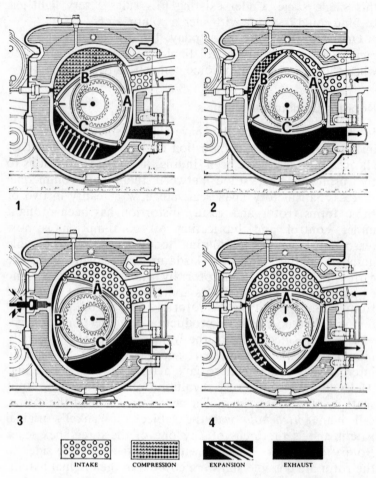

INTAKE   COMPRESSION   EXPANSION   EXHAUST

Fig 9.11   Four-cycle operation of Wankel rotating combustion engine.
An eccentrically mounted three-lobe rotor, turning within an epitro-
choidal combustion casing, drives a centrally mounted output shaft
through an internal gear and pinion. The enclosed volumes at A, B and
C are successively expanded and compressed in the manner of the
four-cycle piston engine. The single sparking plug carries a very high
heat-load since it fires three times per revolution of the rotor, or once
per revolution of the output shaft.

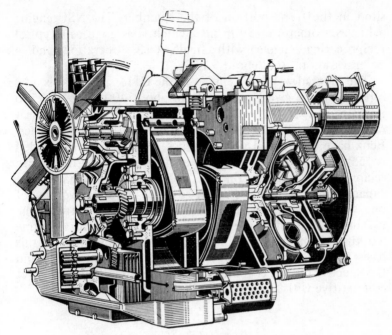

Fig 9.12   The twin-rotor NSU Ro80 engine.

actually works on a four stroke cycle as will be seen from
Fig 9.11.

Good combustion has not been easy to achieve. Not only
is the combustion chamber far too elongated at high
compression ratios, but the physical problems of reducing the
compressed volume for ratios higher than 10 to 1 results in
too much trapped gas between the face of the rotor and the
outer wall of the casing. At low engine speeds the speed of
the unburned gas approaches the sparking plug at a lower rate
than the speed of combustion. The flame front in this case
travels towards the leading portion of the combustion
chamber. At some intermediate speed there is a tendency for
the flame front to remain almost stationary in the region of
the plug and in these conditions it is not easy to obtain good
combustion of the leading part of the mixture. The Mazda
engineers have resorted to two plugs placed well apart to give
good combustion, but the NSU engineers use only one plug

sited in the front portion of the chamber. The NSU engine achieves a bmep of 159 lb/in^2, which is as good as a typical reciprocating engine with single OHC operation and a compression ratio of about 9 to 1.

The Mercedes 4-rotor engine in the C111 sports car is now reported to be giving an output of about 400 b.h.p. at 7500 rev/min and is the only possible contender in sports car racing on the horizon at the moment, although Mercedes-Benz have announced no such plans. The F.I.A. have decided to admit rotating combustion engines in competition with reciprocating engines on the following equivalence: the capacity of the engine is taken as twice the swept volume of one working chamber, i.e. twice the difference between the maximum capacity and the minimum capacity of one working chamber during one revolution of the rotor. On this basis the C111 is equivalent to a 4.8-litre piston engine and the specific output is about 85 b.h.p. per litre. This is not yet competitive with the best of today's piston engines.

SUMMARY

This chapter has been a long one, but we have considered in it so many old ideas and two new ones. Our findings can be summarized as follows:—

1. For engines of 2 litre capacity or greater the four-stroke cycle holds more promise for the future development than the two-stroke cycle.
2. There is little to choose between air-cooling and liquid-cooling. The adoption of an existing fully developed air-cooled engine such as the Porsche could offer a small reduction in total car weight, but the development of an air-cooled engine to the same specific power output as the best liquid-cooled engines is probably more expensive and time-consuming.
3. Turbocharging, using direct fuel injection and excess blower capacity to cool the exhaust valves, is predicted to have a potential power output about 15 per cent greater than current unsupercharged engines in the same competition class (under the existing F.I.A. equivalence ratio

of 1.4). In the next chapter we attempt to predict how many years will elapse before the current engines increase power outputs by 15 per cent.

4. Gas Turbines hold a high potential promise for the future, but this depends upon the availability of new higher-temperature resistant materials from which to make turbine blades. There is then no immediate challenge from the gas turbine.

5. The Wankel engine offers lightness and low-bulk, but the specific power output of the most promising experimental racing/sports engine, the Mercedes C111, is only about 70 per cent of comparative racing piston engines. This engine also does not appear to offer a challenge in the immediate future.

CHAPTER TEN
The Road to Power

THE COMBUSTION CHAMBER

The combustion chamber on a petrol engine serves a dual role and it is the creation of a shape which reconciles its function as the component which houses the inlet and exhaust valves and also encourages good combustion that has engendered so much ingenuity in the past. Despite all the millions of pounds spent on combustion chamber development and combustion research an honest designer, such as Keith Duckworth, will still tell us that he designs his combustion chamber 'by eye'. Beauty, even in combustion chambers, is in the eye of the beholder, and a young designer such as Duckworth, consciously or unconsciously, uses all the empirical know-how that has been passed on to him, all the test-bed experience of an earlier generation, all the accumulated knowledge given in countless engineers' reports to produce a combustion chamber that 'looks right'. In his case, since he is a very good designer, it is right.

Combustion

If such a thing as an ideal combustion chamber exists nobody seems to have found it yet. Porsche use a hemispherical combustion chamber with one inlet and one exhaust valve set at an include angle (between valve centre-lines) of 65°. Ferrari use a pent-roof head with two inlet valves on one side and two exhaust on the other, at an included angle of only 25° Cosworth (Keith Duckworth's design) also use a four-valve pent-roof head on their Formula 1 engine, but in this case the included angle is 32°.

Immediately, when designing an engine, we meet this word 'compromise' between the two functions of the combustion chamber. For good power output we need large inlet valves to prevent the engine from becoming breathless at high speeds and we need large exhaust valves to get rid of the exhaust gases effectively at these same high speeds. For good combustion at low speeds, however, the use of small inlet valves, promotes turbulence in the mixture as it enters the cylinder, and this turbulence persists through the compression stroke to assist the spread of combustion after ignition. The designer of a racing engine learns not to compromise. Power, we stated at the beginning of Chapter Nine, is all that counts; power with a modicum of reliability. So there is no hope of maintaining good combustion at low speeds and the most the designer can hope to achieve is to keep the engine speed where the power curve begins to fall drastically within two-thirds to three-quarters of the peak of the power curve.

Even in a racing engine, where combustion at engine speeds of 10 000 to 12 000 rev/min is completed in about one-thousandth of a second, it is still not correct to regard combustion of the fuel/air mixture as an explosion. An explosion is an uncontrolled chemical reaction producing heat and pressure. In normal combustion in a petrol engine the chemical reaction is fast, but it is a controlled combustion and it is the shape of the combustion chamber and the composition of the hydrocarbons that make up the fuel that contribute most to this reaction remaining controlled. Combustion starts by the ignition of a small volume of mixture at the plug points. From here combustion spreads like an expanding ball of flame; not precisely a ball since the shape of the combustion chamber walls dictate the shape of the expanding flame-front. The rate of spread of this flame-front is dictated by the rate at which heat is transmitted from the flame-front to the next layer of 'the expanding onion' to be burned and by the actual area of the flame-front, which is controlled by the shape of the combustion chamber. If we wish to speed up combustion in any part of the combustion chamber the area of the flame-front at that point must be enlarged. Conversely to slow it down the gas passage must be narrowed.

Heat is transferred from the flame-front to the unburned mixture almost entirely by radiation and convection. The amount of convective heat transfer can be controlled by the degree of turbulence in the gas. The more vigorously the hot burning gas swirls or eddies into the unburned mixture the more rapid will be the spread of combustion. Ricardo's classic experiments about fifty years ago demonstrated how important is the degree of turbulence induced by the 'squish' action of the piston crown as it approaches Top Dead Centre (TDC) against an area of the cylinder head that is purposely designed to have a small clearance at this time. In any engine where smooth combustion is desired it is necessary to encourage a rapid spread of combustion in the early and middle stages of combustion and to slow down the rate of combustion for the final 10 to 20 per cent of the mixture. Ricardo discovered that the last portion of mixture to be burned (which we now call 'the end-gas') has a tendency to become overheated by the advancing flame-front. Under unfavourable conditions this end-gas is liable to burn simultaneously, i.e. to explode or, as the engine technologist calls it, to knock. Later research has shown that knock is caused by certain 'cool-flame' partial oxidation reactions that occur in the end-gas before combustion proper. The chemical reactions involved are very complex and need not concern us here. A mild knock persisting over a few seconds is relatively harmless. The little tinkle we occasionally hear while accelerating at full-throttle with a high-compression engine is not dangerous so long as the tinkle disappears when we reach cruising speed. Prolonged knock while traversing a long straight like the 2.5 miles at Spa-Francorchamps or the 4 miles at Le Mans starts a chain of events where knock raises the temperatures in the zone where it occurs which causes larger amounts of mixture to take part in the knocking reaction, until finally the overheating causes piston failure or the burning of an exhaust valve.

Ricardo showed that knock can be eliminated in two ways: first by changing to a fuel with more resistance to knock and secondly by designing the combustion chamber in such a way that the end-gas is cooled sufficiently to prevent the occurence of uncontrolled combustion. Despite the impressive sums of research and development money concentrated on this one problem since those early days when giants like Ricardo in Great Britain and 'Boss' Kettering in America began to grapple with the problems of knock, the shape of the combustion chamber still leaves much scope for originality and is still bedevilled by the need to give a relatively unhindered flow of the fresh charge into the cylinder and the exhaust gases out.

There are many shapes of combustion chamber and valve layouts still to be found on modern production engines but for sheer power there is still nothing to challenge the two shapes, the hemispherical and the pent-roof. The former is usually preferred on a two-valve head and the latter when four valves are used. Less squish effect is possible on these heads than is possible with the typical push-rod and single OHC production engines, but squish becomes less desirable at high engine speeds and sufficient turbulence to promote rapid combustion can be given by means of 'swirl turbulence' which is a vortex movement induced in the charge entering the cylinder by the shape of the inlet ports.

Harry Weslake, who must have been responsible for the development of more British cylinder heads than anyone alive, measures the amount of swirl induced in this way by means of a special 'swirl-meter' which is a tiny propellor inserted through a gland in the head during the gas-flow experiments. With the correct degree of swirl the rate of propagation of the flame-front across the head is the rate that gives the most efficient combustion for maximum power. In this way the experimental engineer learns how to control combustion even before the engine has run.

Induction and Exhaust

Next to the combustion requirements the other group of factors that control the shape of the combustion chamber are the number, size and disposition of the inlet and exhaust valves. The number and position of the sparking plugs is also important, but on the hemispherical and pent-roof heads there is very little choice left to us after the available area has been almost completely filled with valve heads.

Both types of head grew out of the need to get larger valves into the combustion chamber. Ernest Henry, the brilliant Swiss engineer who designed the 1912 3-litre GP Peugeot, was no doubt taught at school that the two sides of a triangle are always greater than the third so he decided to apply this simple fact by making his combustion chamber like a right-angled triangle with the valves placed at each side of the right-angle. In this way he obtained a very compact combustion chamber and, by providing twin overhead camshafts above the head, he was able to reduce the inertia of his valve system to acceptable proportions. For some reason, which is now obscure, but was probably a lubrication difficulty, the engine was never raced at higher speeds than 3 000 rev/min. At this speed the engine was quite untroubled by valve spring failure, a trouble that beset his contemporaries.

It is intriguing in view of the change in recent Grand Prix engine designs from two valves per head to four to note that Henry adopted four for the two long stroke engines he designed for racing in 1912. His 'Formula Libre' design had a stroke of 200 mm and a bore of 110 mm and it was not surprising that the engine speed was limited to 2200 rev/min. He also appears to have anticipated desmodromic valve operation (i.e. push-pull action), but we have not been able to obtain cross-sectional drawings of these early Henry designs. Very few attempts at designing desmodromic valve operation have been successful. The 1954-55 Mercedes Type W196 straight-8 engine used two cams per valve, one to push on the head of the small tappet and the other to pull on the tappet underface. Extreme care was required in setting clearances, with frequent checks to correct for slight valve seat sinkage. It was a triumph of German engineering discipline over a potentially unreliable system and we are not likely to see a return to this method of valve operation unless some clever designer succeeds in making the valve adjustment automatic.

Moving on a full forty years from the Henry GP engines it is of interest to study Vittorio Jano's design for the 1954 GP formula. The D50 Lancia of 2.48 litres capacity had eight cylinders in two banks of four at 90°. The bore was 73.6 mm and the stroke 73.1 mm, for this was the era of the 'square' engine. Jano actually experimented with a slightly over-square layout, but abandoned it in favour of an almost equal bore and stroke. The valves on each bank were at an included angle of 85° (almost identical to the 1914 Delage). Only one inlet and one exhaust valve per cylinder was used and the compression ratio (on alcohol fuel) had increased from about 6 to 1 in 1914 to about 14 to 1 in 1954. This high

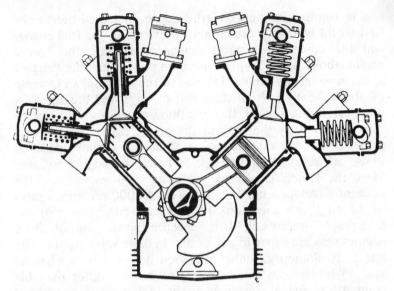

Fig 10.1   Simplified cross-section of 1954 V-8 Lancia-Ferrari Formula
1 engine, Type DS50.

compression ratio made the combustion chamber lose all
semblance of compactness, for the pent-roof shape of the
piston crown fitting the almost identical pent-roof of the
head left a wafer thin combustion space that had a very high
surface to volume ratio (see Fig 10.1). Two plugs per
cylinder helped to propagate the flame across this long
narrow combustion chamber and by the end of the 1954
season this engine was giving a power of 265 b.h.p. (107
b.h.p. per litre). The 1914 Peugeot, very similar in design to
the 3-litre 1912 model, was almost identical in capacity to
the 1954 Lancia, since the 1914 *Coupe de l'Auto* regulations
limited engine size to 2.5 litre. This engine gave 80 b.h.p.
from its four cylinders of 75 mm bore and 140 mm stroke,
which is only 32 b.h.p. per litre. How then had Vittorio Jano
managed to obtain more than a threefold increase in power?
    The increase in compression ratio, using identical fuels,
accounts for only 35 to 40 per cent of this increase in power,
The high latent heat of alcohol fuel improves volumetric
efficiency *at the same engine speed* in comparison with an

engine running on benzole (the racing fuel used before the first world war) and the combined effects of the fuel change and the compression ratio change would give the Lancia engine about 45 to 50 per cent more power than the Peugeot *at the same engine speed.* The rest of the increase, an increase of about 2.5 to 1, is all the result of improved breathing. A practical indication of the breathing efficiency of a set of valves is given by the peak of the power curve. As a general guide we can say that the power of an engine can be doubled if we can persuade it to peak at twice the engine rev/min. Since the Lancia gave peak power at 7500 rev/min and the Peugeot developed maximum power at 3000 rev/min, a ratio of 2.5 to 1, we need look no further for the causes of the remarkable improvement in specific power output from engines that are superficially similar in basic valve layout. The late L. H. Pomeroy, senior expressed it very simply when he said: 'Whoever can make his engine revolve faster than his competitor, and also arrange for it to remain in one piece, will succeed in obtaining the highest power, *always accepting a condition of satisfactory aspiration.*

Two major developments are largely responsible for the improved aspiration that has given the higher rev/min of the modern engines. Today the peak of the power curve occurs, on average, at about 11 000 r.p.m. and the improvement in specific power of about 40 per cent in the 18 years that have passed since the Lancia topped the magical figure of 100 b.h.p. per litre has been the outcome of concentrated experiments in two fields, in the wider use of air-flow rigs and in the wider use of harmonic tuning of induction and exhaust systems.

Air-Flowing
Harry Weslake claims to have invented air-flowing and since 'the Grand Old Man of Rye' first started to improve the induction systems of engines by measuring the air consumption by using a counterbalanced water-sealed gasometer in the year 1922 it is very probable that he was the first. The technique was in use at the time as a means of calibrating coin-in-the-slot household gasmeters. Ricardo used the same technique only two or three years later but the full impact of

air-flowing as a scientific method of improving the volumetric efficiency of an engine was only beginning to be felt in the world of motor racing about twenty years ago. Even in the time of Jano and Lampredi at Scuderia Ferrari almost all the development work was carried out on the dynamometer.

Two basic tools are used in the experimental labs of Weslake Engineering at Rye.

(a) an air-flow rig
(b) a swirl meter

For the air-flow tests wooden replicas of the cylinder head are used since this makes it so easy to make changes in the port dimensions and profiles or to modify the shape of the combustion chamber itself. Air flows in cubic ft per minute for each port and head configuration are measured by accurate flow meters over a range of external pressure heads. For a complete survey of the flows through an inlet valve or exhaust valve it is necessary to make measurements over a range of valve openings, since some port shapes which show up favourably at full valve lift are not as effective when the valve is partially open. By running a whole series of air-flow tests the shape and size of the ports, the valve fillet radius and the parts of the combustion chamber adjacent to the valve head can be gradually modified until the volumetric efficiency reaches the current norm for the particular valve layout (the norm being higher for example for a DOHC layout than for a push-rod OHV with bath-tub head). The theory and practice of air-flowing is discussed in greater detail in the author's companion book 'The Sports Car Engine'.

The second basic tool is the swirl meter, which is a tiny vaned spinner inserted into the dummy combustion chamber. Excessive turbulence, indicated by too high a rate of rotation, will give rough combustion and excessive heat loss to the cooling jackets. Inadequate swirl turbulence will retard the spread of combustion. An engine that requires an excessive ignition advance at the peak of the power curve is usually lacking in swirl turbulence. With the right degree of turbulence (and the experts such as Harry Weslake are too shrewd to disclose any figures) the combustion chamber, the sizes of the valves, the dimensions of the ports and their exact shapes are all matched perfectly to put the peak of the power curve where it should be, at the highest attainable engine rev/min.

Weslake finishes the development of the engine on the dynamometer, but the bulk of the development work on a new head design can be carried out much more quickly and at less expense in the air-flow labs.

Harmonic Induction and Exhaust Systems

The volumetric efficiency of an engine is a measure of an engine's ability to breathe in the new charge at a given engine speed. The volumetric efficiency is the ratio, usually expressed as a percentage, between the volume of air actually inspired per working cycle at standard temperature and pressure and the actual cubic capacity, or swept volume, of the engine.

By providing 'tuned' or harmonic induction and exhaust systems it is not uncommon today to see naturally aspirated engines giving volumetric efficiencies greater than 110 per cent at some point in the power curve. The series of curves given in Fig 10.2 were obtained on a 3.4 litre – D Type Jaguar engine and serve to illustrate how the length of the induction system can be 'tuned' to give a hump in the power curve just where we want it. The use of a very short induction system is obviously to be avoided.

To achieve such high values, however, it is essential to provide a completely separate induction pipe to each cylinder and to have an exhaust system with the branches connected in such a way that regular exhaust intervals occur in the tail pipe or pipes. With a V-8 engine using a two-plane crankshaft, for example, as in the usual American passenger car this would call for cross connections between banks, the two inside exhaust branches on one bank being connected to the two outside branches on the other bank – a veritable snake-pit of pipework. Both induction and exhaust pipe lengths can be tuned to give harmonic charging over portions of the power curve chosen by the designer. Sometimes the lengths of the inlet trumpets are changed to increase or reduce the total length of the induction system to move the

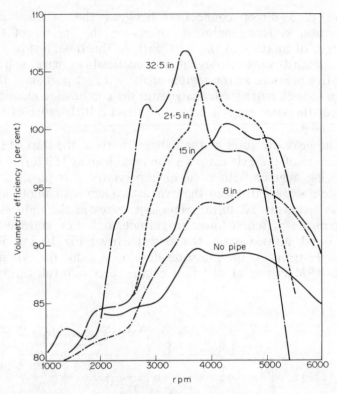

Fig 10.2   Effect of intake pipe length on volumetric efficiency (D Type Jaguar engine).

hump in the power curve where it will be best suited to the requirements of the particular racing circuit.

The theory of harmonic induction and exhaust tuning is very complex and is still not an exact science. Since both pipe systems are subjected to regular pressure impulses as the inlet and exhaust valves open and close both systems can be designed to have pressure waves build up in them of the desired frequency and magnitude. Expressed simply we require a positive pressure wave to arrive at the inlet port just before the inlet valve closes, thus 'ramming in' additional charge. In the exhaust system we require the opposite effect. On engines with large overlaps the movement of exhaust gas out of the combustion chamber, at this time of overlap when there is a direct connection between the exhaust and induction systems, helps to overcome the inertia of the column of mixture in the inlet port. At this time, just before the exhaust valve closes, it is beneficial to have a high negative pressure in the region of the exhaust port since this helps to suck more fresh charge into the combustion chamber and at the same time it helps to extract a little more of the residual gas.

The peak pressures at the exhaust ports at the start of the discharge of the exhaust gases can be as high as 150 lb/in² on a racing engine. With such high pressures it is possible to create a wave pattern in the exhaust system with amplitudes of as much as 30 lb/in². Pressure waves in the induction system are of much lower magnitude, but they still have a profound influence on the power curve. Fig 10.3 shows pressure traces of the pressures developed inside the cylinder of a BRM engine at different engine speeds on full throttle

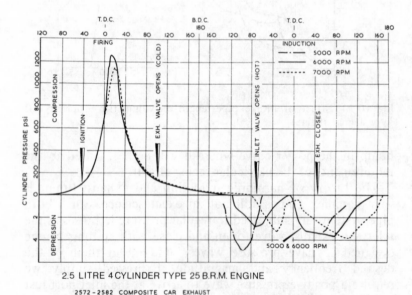

2.5 LITRE 4 CYLINDER TYPE 25 B.R.M. ENGINE

2572-2582 COMPOSITE CAR EXHAUST
.560" LIFT INLET CAMSHAFT   TIMED 62°- 68°   10.4 C.R.   NO SQUISH

Fig 10.3   Indicator diagram for 2.5-litre Type 25 BRM Formula 1 engine. Note changes in pressure during induction process at different speeds.

and full load. In particular it is seen that much higher cylinder pressures are given at 6000 rev/min than at 7000 rev/min. The corresponding traces of cylinder pressure at the time of inlet valve opening show that the favourable low pressures that must have existed in the exhaust ports at this time when running at 6000 rev/min have lowered the pressure inside the combustion chamber to nearly 3 lb/in^2 negative at the moment of inlet valve opening. At 7000 r.p.m., however, the cylinder pressure is only slightly negative when the inlet valve starts to open.

Of course one has to pay for the humps produced in the power curve by harmonic tuning by making hollows in the curve at engine speeds where the exhaust pressures tend to blow back residual gases into the cylinder just as the exhaust valve is closing or when the pressures in the induction system are low at the time of inlet valve closing. The racing driver learns to live with these limitations and the provision of a five speed gearbox, with very close ratios for the top three, helps him to work between a very narrow power band at all times.

VALVE OPERATION

For racing engines, where a limitation on capacity is imposed, as in Group 5 cars competing for the World Championship, where the capacity is limited to 3-litres, push-rod valve operation is unacceptable. The overhead camshafts may be driven from the crankshaft by chains and sprockets, or by timing belts and cogged pulleys as on some of the newer production engines with single OHC or by means of a train of gears. The latter is the most dependable and will give the least variation in valve timing. The manner by which the lift of the cam is transferred to the valve has become resolved on racing engines to two general methods. Most popular today is the use of the bucket tappet (or piston tappet as it sometimes called) where the cam movement is transferred directly to the valve stem. The second and older method is to interpose a rocker between the cam face and the end of the valve stem. It is, naturally, desirable to keep the inertia forces in the whole valve train mechanism as low as possible. High inertia loads demand very strong valve springs to prevent the cam follower from floating at the peak of the cam profile. The use of strong valve springs, as a cure for valve-bounce however, only increases the static load on the valve seats and at low and medium engine speeds the valve seats tend to suffer excessive wear from the high seating pressures.

When comparing the relative inertias of the two systems one must remember that the rockers usually have unequal length arms (see Fig 10.4). Since movement of any portion of the rocker is in proportion to its distance from the fulcrum, a large part of the rocker has very little inertia. It is not surprising then to find that an analysis of the inertia forces involved on three Oldsmobile designs, a push-rod OHV, a rocker OHC and a bucket-tappet OHC, made by Bakonyi of the General Motors Corporation showed that the rocker operated system had 19 per cent lower inertia forces than the

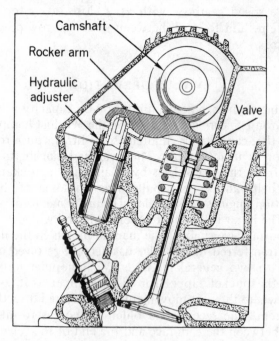

Fig 10.4   Modern example of rocker-actuated SOHC design as used on six-cylinder Pontiac.

directly operated system. The push-rod engine, of course, had much higher inertia than either of the other engines. This fact alone must account for the reluctance of Ferrari and Maserati to adopt the direct acting system for so many years.

The superiority of the overhead camshaft engine is revealed when oscilloscope traces are made of valve lift, velocity and acceleration. Typical traces are given in Fig 10.5

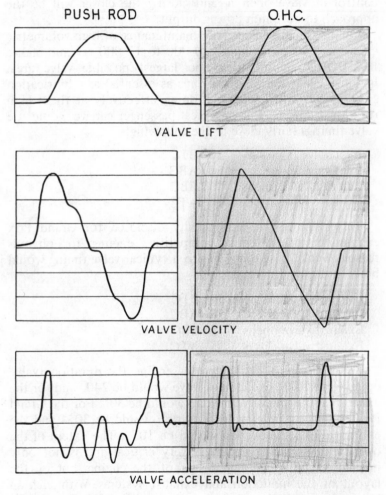

Fig 10.5   Valve bounce: oscilloscope traces of valve lift, velocity and acceleration.

for a push-rod engine and an OHC engine. The springiness and bounce in the push-rod valve operating train results in a series of unpredictable oscillations in the velocity and acceleration curves. These vary with speed, the oscillations being much greater at high speeds. The profile of the cam is not followed at all accurately by the valve and this results in a certain loss in total opening area. The more precise the control of valve opening and closing the closer will be the approach to optimum power output.

For the racing engine, the maintenance of high volumetric efficiences at speeds up to 10 000 to 12 000 rev/min makes the DOHC layout using the largest possible valve area, high-lift cams and large overlaps as essential as a lubrication system that will keep functioning effectively at these high rotational speeds. For a typical passenger car we would use valve timings fairly close to the following:-

Inlet valve opens	10° BTC
Inlet valve closes	50° ABC
Exhaust valve opens	50° BBC
Exhaust valve closes	20° ATC

Valve timings are not usually disclosed for Grand Prix engines or other highly competitive engines for obvious reasons but a close approach to a typical valve timing would be:-

Inlet valve opens	50° BTC
Inlet valve closes	75° ABC
Exhaust valve opens	75° BBC
Exhaust valve closes	55° ATC

For the typical passenger car engine the duration (valve opening period) for the inlet valve would be 240° and for the exhaust 250°; the valve overlap would be 30°. For the Grand Prix engine the inlet valve duration would be 305° and the exhaust 310°; the overlap would be 105°. The extent of the overlap on a racing engine is very critical and is not only influenced by the detail design of the engine, but by the layout of the induction and exhaust systems. With such an extreme valve timing the torque curve falls off rather rapidly at speeds below about 7000 rev/min. A close-ratio gearbox becomes essential with such valve timing.

CARBURATION

After fighting quite a long rear-guard action the carburettor has finally been replaced by fuel injection as the ultimate power producer on naturally aspirated racing engines. It was inevitable. With a separate choke to each cylinder it was difficult to fault the carburettor when tuned correctly on the score of good metering or good distribution. The inherent weakness in the carburettor is its need for a choke (a venturi) to meter the fuel into the air-stream. With the venturi removed it is possible to obtain a slightly higher volumetric efficiency and an improvement in power. A secondary gain achieved by using fuel injection is in the improved atomisation of the fuel. By using relatively high pressures to inject the fuel into the induction port the droplets of fuel are very finely divided. When a carburettor is used, particularly with a large venturi as in a racing engine, the atomization is very poor at the lower operating speeds. This in fact gives the carburetted racing engine an even narrower useable speed range than the fuel injected engine.

Lucas Fuel Injection

The Lucas system has been used extensively on European racing engines for nearly 10 years and appeared in its original form on the D Type Jaguars in 1956. A gear type pump is provided to supply fuel at the injection pressure and a reciprocating shuttle or shuttles in conjunction with a rotary distributor is used to meter the fuel in the appropriate quantities, as dictated by engine demand, to injection nozzles fitted to each inlet port. Control of the amount of fuel metered by each shuttle is arranged by varying the stroke as shown in Fig 10.6. A mixture control stop is moved inwards by means of a wedge and roller device and an induction pressure operated diaphragm or piston. When the plate type throttle valve is opened to admit more air to the engine, the induction pressure rises (the manifold depression is reduced), the control wedge falls under the action of the control spring and the shuttle valve stroke is increased to produce a longer injection period to the injection nozzle. A datum adjuster is provided to allow fine tuning to be carried out at the circuit to suit the particular altitude and temperature conditions.

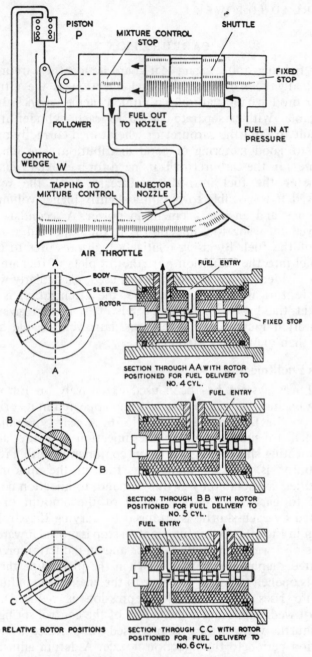

Fig 10.6   Operation of the Lucas fuel injection system.

The slide type throttle plates run against hardened steel rollers and give 100 per cent opening of the inlet tract at full throttle.

Bosch Fuel Injection

Although Bosch have now developed an electronic control system to meter timed impulses to each fuel injector the type of injection system still favoured in racing circles is the older jerk-pump mechanical system which historically is a development of the famous Bosch Diesel injection system. Bosch mechanical fuel injection uses a separate cam-operated plunger for each cylinder with output controlled by the position of helical ports in annular sleeves surrounding the plungers. Rotation of the sleeves to vary the cut-off point of injection, thus varying the quantity of fuel injected per stroke, is performed by a toothed rack which engages teeth machined on the outside of each sleeve. The complex control system of the Bosch system is shown in Fig 10.7.

FORMULA FOR SUCCESS

It is no new discovery that the secret of success in the higher echelons of sports car racing is to use a power unit with as little de-tuning as experience dictates, from that highest echelon of all, Formula 1. Ettore Bugatti never hesitated to use his racing engines in his sports cars and that most successful of post-war racing sports engines, the Mercedes 300SLR was really an enlarged version of the Formula 1 Type W196. Enzo Ferrari has used GP engines in his racing sports cars wherever possible, even though the factory at Maranello can manufacture parts for completely new designs of engine as quickly as most of us can knock together a new garden shed.

The current limitation of 3-litre for Racing Sports Cars (Group 5) entered for the World Championship has been a wonderful turn of events for the Ferrari organisation since their flat-12 Type 312B engine had been developed to the stage where it could challenge the Formula 1 Cosworth V-8 engine by the end of 1971 and this flat-12 engine, slightly de-tuned was an obvious choice for the 3-litre Group 5 Ferrari sports

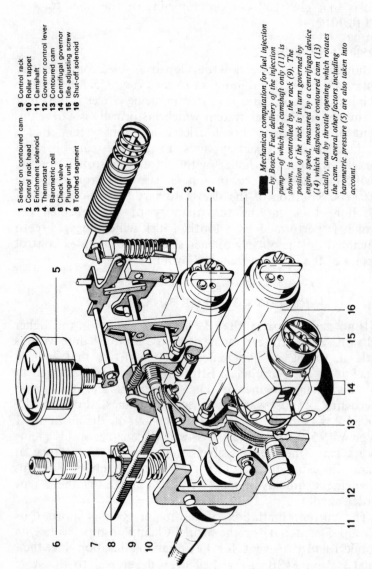

1 Sensor on contoured cam
2 Control rack head
3 Enrichment solenoid
4 Thermostat
5 Barometric cell
6 Check valve
7 Plunger unit
8 Toothed segment
9 Control rack
10 Roller tappet
11 Camshaft
12 Governor control lever
13 Contoured cam
14 Centrifugal governor
15 Idle adjusting screw
16 Shut-off solenoid

Mechanical computation for fuel injection
—by Bosch. Fuel delivery of the injection
pump—of which the camshaft only (11) is
shown, is controlled by the rack (9). The
position of the rack is in turn governed by
engine speed, measured by a centrifugal device
(14) which displaces a contoured cam (13)
axially, and by throttle opening which rotates
the cam. Several other factors including
barometric pressure (5) are also taken into
account.

Fig 10.7   Bosch mechanical fuel injection.

car to be used in 1972. The de-tuned camshafts give slightly less overlap and the inlet trumpets are longer to give more torque at lower engine speeds than the GP version. The maximum speed is limited to 10 800 rev/min against 12 600 rev/min in the Formula 1 engine and the maximum power is believed to be about 430 b.h.p., which is about 50 b.h.p. less than the 1973 Formula 1 engine.

The need to detune an engine and the extent of this operation depends upon the designer's judgement of the engine's ability to withstand long periods of full-throttle operation over a race of much longer duration than a typical Grand Prix. In the case of Le Mans this total duration is of course 24 hours and the percentage of driving time spent at full throttle on this hard course is 65–70 per cent of total time. Nürburgring, on the other hand, notorious as a tester of suspension and handling, is much less severe on the engine since full throttle on this twisty course is only used for about 40 per cent of the lap time.

The Ghost of Dr. Lanchester

Certain guide lines have been established to assist the designer in his choice of his basic design parameters and few are as important as the dimensions of the bore and stroke. It was in 1906 that Dr F. W. Lanchester, as brilliant a mathematician as he was an engineer, read a paper to the Institution of Mechanical Engineers (Proc. I.A.E., Vol. 1, 1906–7) in which he demonstrated that the specific power of an engine of constant stroke/bore ratio varies almost directly as the piston area. There are two ways in which we can design an engine to have a large piston area for a limited cubic capacity. The first is to reduce the stroke and increase the bore. Dr Lanchester recommended such a step and at this time the stroke/bore ratio was usually about 2 to 1. The British system of car taxation did not encourage this move, since cars were taxed at that time on a formula that was based only on the piston area. In designing racing cars, however, one is not subjected to such legislation and by about 1950 the typical racing engine was now 'square' in design, i.e. with a stroke/bore ratio of about unity. Typical stroke/bore ratios in racing engines are now in the bracket 0.70 to 0.85 and it is doubtful if they will drop much lower than 0.70 in the near future since the shape of the combustion chamber begins to become far too elongated to achieve good combustion at the high compression ratios used in racing engines.

The second way to increase piston area from a given cubic capacity is to increase the number of cylinders. Henry's 3-litre GP Peugeot of 1912 had four cylinders of 78 mm bore and the piston area was 191.2 cm^2 (28.6 in^2). The stroke, in common with engines of the day, was very long, 156 mm. The Cosworth DFV Formula 1 engine is a V-8 with a bore of 85.7 mm and the piston area is 461 cm^2 (71.5 in^2); the Ferrari 312B is a flat-12 with a bore of 77mm and the piston area is 559 cm^2 (86.5 in^2). All these are 3-litre engines but the modern ones by using short strokes and large numbers of cylinders have as much as three times the piston area of the four cylinder Peugeot.

Unfortunately, the use of very large numbers of cylinders tends to increase the weight of an engine. The H-16 3-litre BRM engine ran into serious torsional vibration problems in its system of twin-geared crankshafts and after re-design in an attempt to alleviate this vibration the final weight was 520 lb. It is doubtful if a reliable H-16 could be made for a lower weight than 450 lb, yet the weight of the V-8 Cosworth is only 355 lb. The V-8 engine is also a shorter engine than its rivals and this feature in a rear-engined layout is a distinct asset.

Let us take a closer look at this famous engine. The general layout of the Cosworth-Ford GP engine differs considerably from the earlier successful Indianapolis Ford DOHC design and indeed it can be said to depart radically from the classic DOHC layout established by Ferrari, Maserati and Lancia where the valves are steeply angled at an included angle of from 65° to as much as 80°. Keith Duckworth chose an included angle as low as 32°.

Tests on an airflow rig at the Ford laboratories in Dearborn had already established that a four valve head will give superior breathing to a two valve head, even on an engine with such a low stroke/bore ratio as 0.77. Even so the designers of the American Ford DOHC engine for Indianapolis adopted an included angle between the valve stems of

70°, i.e. the classic layout. Keith Duckworth, however, reasoned that a less steeply angled head would improve the shape of the combustion chamber and, incidentally, reduce the weight of the piston. His earlier work on a Formula 2 engine with a 40° included angle encouraged him to reduce the angle on his new engine to 32°. His decision was vindicated later on the test-bed when his two relatively small 1.32 inch diameter inlet valves and two exhaust valves of only 1.14 inch diameter where shown to breathe well enough for the power curve to peak at 9000 rev/min (increased to 10 000 rev/min by 1972). The use of small valves greatly reduces the problems caused by high inertia loads on valve springs and valve seats, an everpresent source of trouble on two-valve heads. With such a small included angle between the valves there was no need to provide the customary twin 'rocker-boxes' and the whole valve gear and centrally located sparking plugs could be enclosed very neatly and lightly under a single rectangular cover over each cylinder head. A separate cam carrier casting was interposed between each cylinder head and its cover. These castings carried the guides for the 32 piston-type tappets and the four chilled cast-iron camshafts.

The bore and stroke of the engine is 85.7 mm by 64.7 mm, giving a stroke/bore ratio of 0.755 and a swept volume of 2993 c.c. The compression ratio of 11 to 1 is typical for today's Formula 1 engines running on Premium pump fuel of 101–102 Octane Number (Motor Method). The two banks of cylinders are at an included angle of 90°, the conventional layout for most American engines, and the left-hand block is placed 3/8 inch ahead of the right-hand to allow for the offset of the left and right-hand connecting rods which share common crankpins. The typical American V-8 has a four-throw crankshaft with the two middle throws set at 90° to the outer throws. This crank throw arrangement is preferable in the passenger car engine, since it gives perfect balance of primary and secondary forces, leaving only a small secondary couple unbalanced. Unfortunately the firing order required for this crank layout gives irregular firing intervals between cylinders on the same bank. Harmonic induction charging, which we described earlier in the chapter, demands an exhaust system with regular time intervals between connected branches. To achieve this with such a crankshaft (usually called a two-plane crankshaft) requires the inner exhaust branches from one bank of cylinders to cross over the engine to join the outer branches from the opposite bank and vice versa. The resultant tangle of pipes not only adds to the overall weight of the car, but involves a penalty of increased drag since the maximum cross-section of the car (on a Formula 1 car) occurs in this region. Keith Duckworth calculated that the increased roughness introduced by the unbalanced secondary forces that must occur when a single-plane crankshaft is used was more acceptable than such a tangle of pipework. The single-plane crankshaft does give regularly spaced firing intervals on the same bank. It is therefore a simple matter to run all four branches on the same side into a common tail pipe and obtain harmonic exhausting.

Despite the success and reliability of the Cosworth DFV Formula 1 engine over a period of four seasons of racing the ring of truth in Dr Lanchester's elegant mathematics is gradually being demonstrated by the increasing outputs of the flat-12 Ferrari Type 312B. At the start of the 1973 season the Ferrari is producing 480 b.h.p. at 12 000 rev/min against the Series 12 DFV Cosworth which now delivers 450 b.h.p. at 10 500 rev/min.

Donald Bastow's Formula

It is a long time since Dr Lanchester set an example by applying dimensional theory to engine design and many engineers have since proposed modifications to his formula in the light of practical experience of the actual powers produced by series of engines with identical family characteristics. In a recent communication to the Journal of Automotive Engineering (January, 1972) Donald Bastow, B.Sc.,F.I.Mech.E. suggested this new formula based on an analysis he has recently made on a series of modern engines:—

$H.P. = N \times R^{0.34} \times \phi^{0.5} \times D^{1.65} \times S^{0.5}$ times a constant (depending on common factors in the series of engines, such as valve operation, etc)

TABLE 10.1

Simplified Bastow Formula: b.h.p. per litre $= \dfrac{C}{D^{0.35} \times S^{0.5}}$

Year	Make	Type	Designer	Capacity litres	Bore D mm	Stroke S mm	Number of cylinders	Cylinder arrangement	Number of Valves per cylinder	Value of C	b.h.p. (dyno)	Engine rev/min at peak	Actual b.h.p. per litre	Formula b.h.p. per litre
1912	Peugeot	Formula Libre	E. Henry	7.595	110	200	4	In-line	4	1700	175	2200	23	23.5
1912	Peugeot	GP	E. Henry	2.98	78	156	4	In-line	4	1700	90	3000	30	29.5
1914	Mercedes	GP	P. Daimler	4.490	93	165	4	In-line	4	1700	115	2800	26	27.0
1922	Miller	Indy	H. Miller	1.983	59.7	88.9	8	In-line	4	2300	120	5000	60	58.5
1922	Vauxhall	T.T.	H. R. Ricardo	2.999	85	132	4	In-line	2	2300	129	4500	43	42.2
1923	Sunbeam	GP	Bertarione	1.990	67.0	94.0	6	In-line	2	2300	102	5000	51	54.2
1923	Delage	GP	H. Plancton	1.985	51.3	80.0	12	60° V	4	2300	120	—	60	64.3
1954	Lancia/Ferrari	DS50 F1	Jano/Lampredi	2.489	73.6	73.1	8	90° V	2	4300	275	7500	111	112
1954	Ferrari	625 F1	Lampredi	2.490	94.0	90.0	4	In-line	2	4300	230	7000	92	92.5
1955	Mercedes-Benz	W196	Uhlenhaut	2.490	76.0	68.8	8	In-line	2	4300	290	8750	116	114
1964	Coventry Climax	F1	Hassan	1.495	67.8	51.6	8	90° V	4	4500	200	10 000	134	140
1965	Ferrari	F1	Chiti	1.487	64.0	57.8	8	90° V	2	4500	210	11 000	141	137.5
1965	BRM	F1	Berthon	1.498	69.85	48.89	8	90° V	2	4500	220	11 750	147	145.5
1965	Honda	F1	Nakenura	1.496	56.5	49.5	12	60° V	2	4500	230	12 000	154	156
1971	Porsche	917	Mezger	4.998	86.8	70.35	12	Flat	2	5300	630	8300	126	132
1972	BRM	F1	Woods	2.999	74.63	57.2	12	60° V	4	5300	450	11 500	151	155
1972	Cosworth-Ford	DFV, Series 12	Duckworth	2.993	85.7	64.8	8	90° V	4	5360	440	10 000	147	139
1972	Ferrari	312P		2.989	77.0	53.5	12	60° V	4	5300	480	12 600	160	158

207

N = number of cylinders
R = compression ratio
ϕ = a constant based on the limiting stresses in the materials of construction.

The author suggests we can simplify this formula for racing engines since no limitation on available materials (such as cost) exists and almost identical compression ratios are used in DOHC engines running on the same fuel. Therefore, for DOHC racing engines the formula becomes:—

$$H.P. = \text{Constant} \times N \times D^{1.65} \times S^{0.5}$$

In terms of *specific* power this becomes:—

$$\text{bhp per litre} = \frac{C}{D^{0.35} \times S^{0.5}}$$

where C = Constant for a particular era
D = Bore, mm
S = Stroke, mm.

Table 10.1 has been compiled to illustrate how well this formula relates to the powers actually developed by

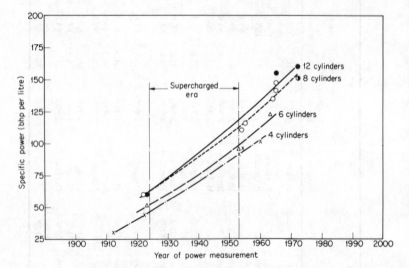

Fig 10.8   Specific power outputs of 1.5—3-litre unsupercharged racing engines with 4, 6, 8 and 12 cylinders.

DOHC racing engines since the time of Ernest Henry. The following values of C have been found to apply to the different periods of engine development. Supercharged engines have of course been omitted.

1912–1914	$C = 1700$
1922–1923	$C = 2300$
1954–1955 (alcohol fuel)	$C = 4300$
1964–1965 (pump fuel)	$C = 4500$
1971–1972 (pump fuel)	$C = 5300$

Taking the actual specific powers produced by these engines we have drawn the graphs in Fig 10.8 to illustrate the influence of the number of cylinders. From this we can predict that by 1980, if current trends are maintained, the DOHC engine should be giving a specific power of 175 b.h.p. per litre. The only known development we can see challenging this performance would be the adoption of turbo charging.

CHAPTER ELEVEN
The Transmission

TORQUE MULTIPLICATION

It is common knowledge that the internal combustion engine has a limited range to its useful operating speeds and the need to vary the speed ratio between the power unit and the driven wheels is not in dispute. The speed changes can be in finite steps as in the normal manual gearbox or 'infinitely' variable by means of a torque convertor, or selectively variable as when two or three gears and a torque convertor unit are used to cover chosen speed ranges as in the typical automatic gearbox.

The useful torque range of a racing engine is even more limited than is the case with touring engines. When a manual gearbox is used, which is the normal practice, the number of gears required to achieve the best lap times could be four, five or even six. The current 3-litre Ferraris and Alfa Romeos use a five-speed box, whereas no more than four were found necessary for the 5-litre Porsche 917.

It is usual today to find that a racing gearbox provides very close ratios for the three or four gears that are needed to keep the engine operating close to its maximum torque figures on the various corners of the circuit, leaving a relatively wide step down to bottom gear. Bottom gear is therefore geared low enough to get the car away from a standing start and is only needed again for the very slow corners, such as Mulsanne (35–40 m.p.h.) and Arnage (40–45 m.p.h.) on the Le Mans circuit.

The Effective Torque Range

The choice and number of ratios to give optimum acceleration will depend upon the power and torque characteristics of the particular engine. A very peaky torque curve, such as that on the Ferrari 312P, which is very close to Formula 1 tune, or on the Matra MS670 with a near Grand-Prix V-12

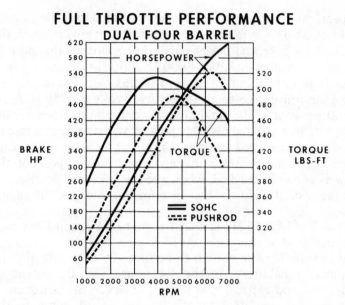

Fig 11.1   Power and torque curves for two Ford competition engines.

engine, which won at Le Mans in 1972, must work all the time within the top 80 per cent of the maximum speed range. A drop in ratio from 4.0 to 1 in second gear to 3.0 to 1 in third gear would drop the engine speed far to low for effective acceleration. Fig 11.1 will serve to illustrate this point on two engines that are far less peaky in their torque characteristics than any of the current racing engines. The dotted curves show the b.h.p. and torques developed by the 427 in³ (7 litres) Ford push-rod engine after several years of competition development. The full-line curves are the comparitive values achieved by the SOHC 427 in³ engine in which Ford Motor Company developed during 1964, using the major components of the block/crankcase section of the 427 push-rod OHV engine. In this comparison both engines were fitted with dual four-barrel carburettors and had similar valve timings. In passing, it is of interest to notice how the change from a slant-head push-rod OHV design to a hemispherical-head SOHC design has improved breathing and combustion, not only to improve power output as one might expect, but also to broaden the torque curve. Mechanical limitations do not in fact allow the SOHC engine to reach the peak of its potential power curve, but assuming this peak to be in the region of 7500–8000 rev/min the torque curve is seen to peak at about 50 per cent of this speed. In the case of the push-rod engine the torque curve peaks at 4750 rev/min, or 60 per cent of the maximum power rev/min. Moreover the drop off in torque above this peak is very rapid, at a rate of about 7 per cent reduction in torque for the next 12 per cent (1000 rev/min) increase in engine speed. The peak of the power curve is reached when the incremental decrease in torque exactly equals the incremental increase in engine speed.

The Ford GT40 Mk II which won at Le Mans in 1965 used the push-rod version of the 427 engine, but the carburation and camshafts were chosen to de-tune the engine to give the required reliability for the 24 hour race. By means of induction and exhaust ram tuning, however, the power curve was suitably modified to give a very useful hump in the region of 5000 rev/min. The actual power curve of the Le Mans engine is given in Fig 11.2. Since the step-up ratio between second and third gear and between third and top was close to 1.2 acceleration was much improved by the location of this hump. In second gear the car would accelerate up to 140 m.p.h. (6100 rev/min). the change to third would drop the speed to about 138 m.p.h. (0.5 seconds change time) at which road speed the engine speed in third would be exactly 5000 rev/min. Similarly the change to top gear was designed again to drop the engine speed once more right on the peak of the tuning hump at 5000 rev/min. A fifth gear would have been necessary to complete this progression in a logical manner, but a race-proven 5-speed box was not available, so the step between first and second gear was made very large (a step of 1.55 to 1 against the 1.2 to 1 of the other ratios. This was within the practical torque range of the engine and the change from first to second gear did actually coincide with a second tuning peak in the power curve at about 3900 rev/min. A drop down to first gear was in any case only required twice in the whole circuit (at Mulsane and Arnage). This gearing was almost perfect for Le Mans, but a

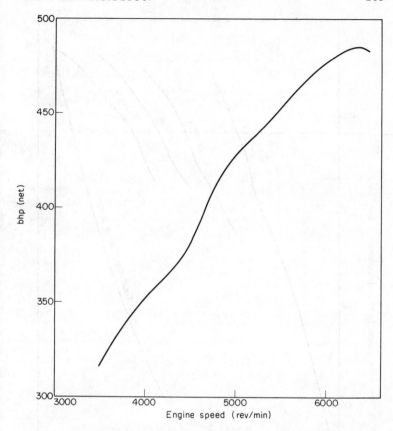

Fig 11.2   Power curve for GT40 Mark II engine in 1965 Le Mans tune.

marginal improvement might have been made if a 5-speed box had been available.

The author has calculated the power curves in the four gears against the road speeds in each gear. The data was supplied by the Ford Motor Company. The curve of total drag horse-power for the GT40 Mk II is also given in Fig 11.3. The difference between the net power available and the drag horse-power is the power available for acceleration. In bottom gear it reaches about 390 b.h.p. and even at a speed of 150 m.p.h. in third gear there is still 220 horse-power available.

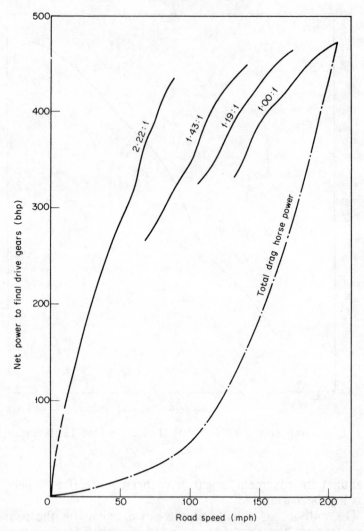

Fig 11.3   Available powers in each gear of GT40 Mark II. Total power absorbed in drag is also plotted. Power available for acceleration at any given road speed is difference between power curve in appropriate gear and total drag power curve.

The GT40 Fords were designed with only one object in mind – to win at Le Mans. In general a racing sports car must be capable of racing on any given circuit at short notice. One cannot easily make changes in the step-up ratios, but the practice is to use two alternatives to match the engine and transmission to the particular circuit. The first change is that of final drive ratio, a lower ratio (numerically) being used for a faster circuit. The second change that is easy to accomplish ts to change the length of the intake trumpets, thus varying the position of the intake ram hump on the power curve. Occasionally one sees mechanics sawing off lengths of exhaust piping, but this is usually a sign of desperation.

The Transaxle

Racing cars with rear or mid-engine location usually have the gearbox and final drive reduction gears incorporated in a single unit called a transaxle. How this is achieved in a neat package can be seen from Fig 11.4 which is a schematic

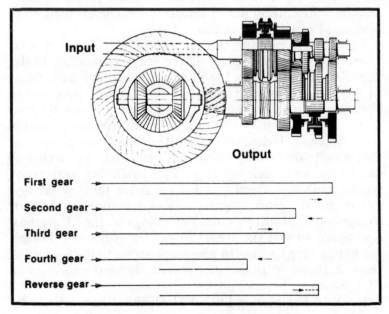

Fig 11.4   Schematic cross-section of ZF transaxle.

cross-section of a ZF transaxle giving four forward ratios and reverse. This is the normal arrangement, with the gearbox behind the final drive gears. It is of course possible to put the gear box in front of the rear wheels. With this arrangement the driver must be seated further forward, but the overall siting of the major masses gives a small reduction in the polar moment of inertia and this as we stated in Chapter Five improves the speed of response of the car to steering forces.

The Type T33TT Alfa Romeo Group 5 Team cars appeared in 1972 with the transaxle re-designed with the gearbox inboard and Porsche Type 908 have raced with the gear box behind (908/2) and ahead (908/3). The scheme is not without its disadvantages. It is far more difficult to make a change of final drive ratio, sometimes taking several hours. It also results in a shortening of the input shaft. The resilience of this shaft, by its ability to absorb shock loads in the manner of a torsion bar, can sometimes save the gear teeth from failure. There is very little that is good in the use of a propellor shaft in the traditional front engine-rear drive layout, but the torsional wind-up that the propellor shaft absorbs under the abuses of savage clutch engagements must have saved many back axles from failure.

The ZF Company or Zahnradfabrik Friedrichshaven A G, to give them their full name, started life as a subsidiary of the Zeppelin Foundation in 1915 and no doubt they made some of the components that went into the Zeppelin that tried to eliminate the author when still a babe in arms. They did have more success when they turned to gearboxes and transmission systems. Today, in fact, their name is recognized throughout the world as in the first rank for technical excellence and high quality. The baulk-ring system of synchromesh was developed by ZF about thirty years ago and is still the most effective way of achieving fast smooth changes on a manual gearbox. For racing cars the ZF gearbox is designed so that the mainshaft can be withdrawn through the bolted rear housing to give quick access to the final drive gears. A choice of three ratios is available for the majority of ZF transaxles.

Hewland Engineering Ltd. of Maidenhead have captured a

large slice of the Grand Prix transmission business in recent years. In 1972 Lola and Matra Simca both used Hewland transaxles at Le Mans. This unit was the DG300 Mark 2 with five forward speeds, designed to transmit the torque of an engine of up to 4.5 litres. No synchromesh device is provided, gear engagement being given by dog-clutches as in so many robust gearboxes of the vintage era. Third, fourth and fifth gears are interchangeable; first and second fixed. The choice of gearing is wide. The gears run on caged needle roller bearings and the differential and crown-wheel assembly runs on taper roller bearings for which the correct pre-load can be set by means of shims. Lubrication of the gearbox section is by splash but a special pump is provided for lubrication of the final drive. All gears and shafts are of heat-treated nickel-chrome steel, the selector forks are of aluminium bronze and the casing of the transaxle is a magnesium casting. Clutch operation is by slave cylinder located on the side of the gearbox. The total weight of the DG 300 Mark 2 unit is 118 lb.

AUTOMATIC TRANSMISSION

The use of automatic transmission on a racing sports car, outrageous as it may seem to the goggles and gauntlet gang, can be justified on two grounds, but only if it can be proved to be competitive with the manual gearbox. It can be justified in that it relieves the driver of some physical and mental effort, often at a time when his full attention should be directed elsewhere. Secondly it provides a very effective shock absorber between the engine flywheel and the final drive gears. Modern racing clutches tend to be harsh in action; they must be to transmit so much power without the slightest trace of slip when fully engaged. With a manual gearbox one clumsy gearchange can shear a drive shaft or break off a gear tooth. An automatic transmission removes this danger. But is the automatic as efficient and can we afford the weight?

To answer this we need to consider a little more fully the manner of operation of modern automatic transmissions.

The Two Basic Sections

Modern automatic transmission combine in different arrangements two engineering transmission components, the hydraulic torque convertor and the epicyclic reduction gear. A control system is also required to select the appropriate gears automatically at the right time.

The Torque Convertor

The earliest torque converters were made in Germany by Föttinger, who patented the system in 1905 and first applied it to marine drive in 1908. The maximum efficiency of his device was only 83 per cent. Torque converters were developed for automotive use about forty years ago in Great Britain. The Lysholm-Smith Torque Converter used widely on buses made by Leyland Motors Ltd. was one successful application. The White Hydro Torque Drive (a development of the Schneider Converter) first appeared on American buses in 1946 and was soon followed by passenger car applications such as the Buick Dynaflow.

Basically these converters all use the same principle. A simple hydraulic coupling can be made into a converter by the addition of a third element. The simple hydraulic coupling has two elements, a pump wheel (or impellor) and a turbine wheel (or runner). These two elements are similar in appearance and consist of two inward facing saucer-like members with radial vanes on the convex faces of the saucers. The component shown on the left of Fig 11.5 is simply a casing to enclose the hydraulic fluid. Fluid is directed from the blades of the pump member at the blades of the turbine member as the pump member rotates. Since the speed of this member is higher than that of the turbine member the higher centrifugal force of the pumping side makes the fluid rotate inside the vanes upwards and outwards across to strike the vanes on the turbine side, the fluid returning to the pump side across the lower section of the blades. In this way energy is transferred quickly from the pump member to the turbine member and the speed of the latter very quickly approaches that of the former – but not quite. There is always a small percentage slip, as little as 1 per cent when the torque being

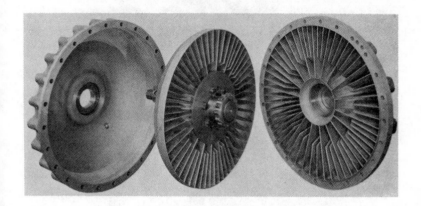

Fig 11.5   Simple fluid coupling.

transmitted is low and as much as 4 per cent nearer full load. This slip represents loss of power which is dissipated in heating up the fluid.

To make this coupling into a torque converter we need to interpose a reactor member between the pump and the turbine. A cut-away view of a three-element torque converter is shown in Fig 11.6. The blades in the pump, reactor and turbine are no longer straight radial blades, but are curved at different angles to give the required characteristic torque ratio curves of the type shown in Fig 11.7. In this type of converter the reactor element is fixed to the casing. The term 'racing' used in the figure refers to the runaway condition where no torque is transmitted to the output shaft.

Modern torque converters as used in automotive transmissions have free-wheeling reactors and are more correctly described as polyphase converters, since multiple reactors are used, each having different blade angles so that they will automatically adjust their speeds to the changing fluid speeds. Typical performance data for one having three reactors are given in Fig 11.8.

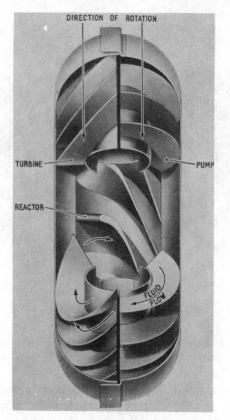

DIRECTION OF ROTATION

TURBINE

PUMP

REACTOR

FLUID FLOW

Fig 11.6   Three-element torque converter.

The Stepped Gear Train

The torque converter is not the complete answer to our requirements. It gives a smooth change in torque over its operating speed range, but the torque ratio change we require for a racing sports car is about 3.5 to 4.0 to 1 and if we were to obtain this from one torque converter it would involve a great sacrifice in efficiency. In top gear a manual gearbox will give an efficiency of about 99 per cent. A good torque converter will approach 93 per cent, but only if we limit the torque ratio to about 2 to 1. To overcome this limitation we use a system of epicyclic reduction gears (see Fig 11.9) to

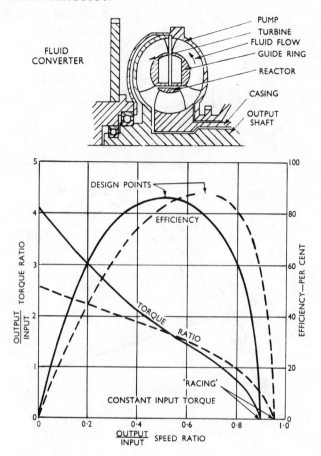

Fig 11.7   Performance data for typical fluid converter.

give a series of steps in the gear train in the manner of the simple geared steps we use in a manual gear box. The epicyclic gear train is used since it lends itself to automatic operation. Engagement of the train only requires the locking of the annulus gear ring by means of a friction band.

The Borg-Warner three-speed automatic transmission, shown diagrammatically in Fig 11.10, could be used on a racing car. It incorporates a direct top gear. This can be engaged automatically at some chosen speed, such as 150

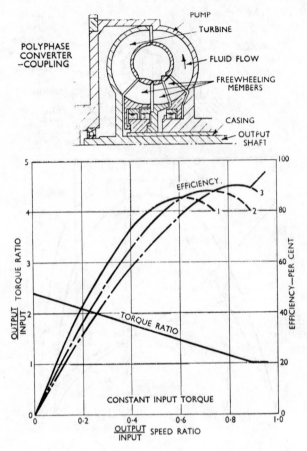

Fig 11.8 .Performance data for polyphase converter.

m.p.h., by means of a simple disc clutch. Above this speed the efficiency would be as high as a manual gearbox in top gear. When direct drive is disengaged a simple reactor free-wheeling torque converter will be in use. Gear trains C and E are locked to engage this intermediate gear. To engage low gear C is released and D locked. Reverse gear is given by locking only the brake band on train B.

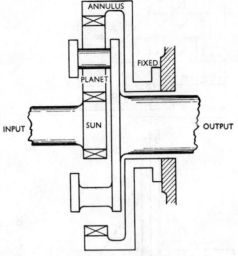

Simple Epicyclic Reduction Gear

An epicyclic gear train comprises a sun wheel and an annulus gear
with planet wheels in constant-mesh with both sun annulus. The
planet wheels are journalled on a planet carrier. In the diagram a
reduction gear train is shown. The sun is driven, the annulus is
fixed, and the planets thus caused the roll round inside the annulus,
carrying the plant carrier with them. If the annulus is arrested by a
brake band the gear train may be made operative by simply applying
the brake.

Fig 11.9   Simple epicyclic reduction gear.

Control Systems

Automatic transmissions use sophisticated hydraulic servos
and relay valves to engage and disengage the gear trains at the
designed combinations of engine speed and manifold vacuum.
Manual over-ride is provided and would of course be essential
on a racing car. To keep noise levels low it is customary on
passenger cars to set the controls to give automatic speed
change to a higher ratio at no more than two-thirds of
maximum engine speed. On a racing car one could set the
controls to allow maximum permissible engine speed to be
reached before the next gear change occurred. Comparative
performance curves for a three-ratio automatic and four ratio
manual gearbox are given in Fig 11.11. The manual ratios are

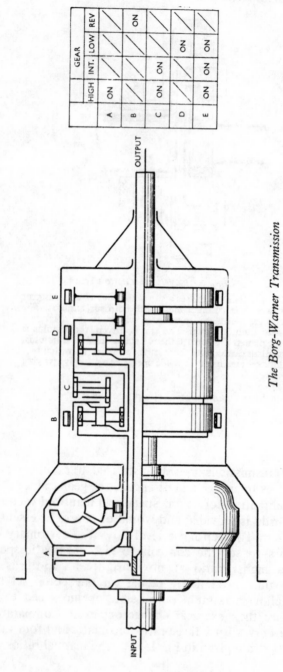

	HIGH	GEAR INT.	LOW	REV
A	ON			
B				ON
C	ON	ON		
D			ON	
E	ON	ON	ON	

The Borg-Warner Transmission

Fig 11.10 Borg-Warner three-speed automatic transmission. This transmission has a three-element torque converter with an automatically oil-operated epicyclic running gear. A direct drive clutch is provided for top gear.

224

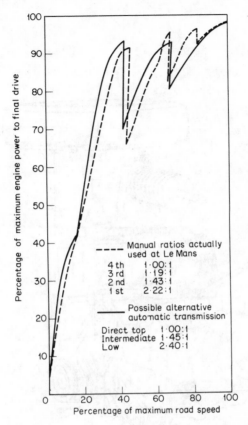

Fig 11.11   Comparative power curves for automatic and manual transmission.

those actually used on the winning Ford at Le Mans in 1966. The automatic transmission is the author's alternative scheme in which a direct top would be used in conjunction with two planetary intermediates, the first giving a ratio of 1.45 and the second giving 2.40. The curves show that the automatic box would give improved acceleration up to 65 per cent of maximum speed (about 130 m.p.h.). Above that speed the two close ratios of the manual box would give slightly improved acceleration. The use of 4 or 5 automatically-operated ratios or a more sophisticated polyphase convertor would probably

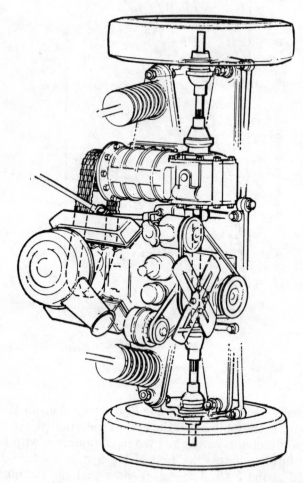

Fig 11.12 Layout of Oldsmobile FWD on Toronado. A chain drive is used between torque converter and automatic gearbox.

match the manual box in the middle speed range and beat it at the lower speeds, but it is difficult to see how such a complicated transmission system could be made without a substantial increase in weight. We therefore are left with the traditional system, but the margin is very close and will no doubt be closed completely in the near future. Jim Hall has been a keen advocate for automatics for many years – and Jim has an uncanny knack of being right.

Front Wheel Drive

The problems of FWD are largely concerned with space. The British Leyland Mini is usually quoted as an object lesson in economical packaging. It could hardly be more compact, or unfortunately, less accessible. The cross-mounted engine transmission layout is limited to small and medium-sized engines. One could hardly apply this technique to an FWD car like the Oldsmobile. The problem presented to this design group was to install a 455 in^3 (7.5 litres) engine and at the side of this an automatic transmission with 4 ratios, all inside a track of 5 ft 3½ in, which is close to the average for a full-size American sedan. How a chain drive was used to achieve this is shown in the sketch of Fig 11.12.

In the Taunus FWD saloon a hollow drive shaft was used so that the final drive could be placed on the same level as the crankshaft (see Fig 11.13). A long quill shaft passed through the hollow pinion shaft to take the drive from the clutch to the rear of the gearbox. This incidentally gave a useful length of torsionally resilient shaft between the clutch and the gearbox.

Four Wheel Drive

In Chapter One we gave some of the historical background to the development of reliable universal joints for front wheel drive cars, which are of course also necessary when we take the drive to all four wheels. In Chapters Four and Five we considered the benefits to be gained in acceleration and cornering from 4WD. In this chapter we shall consider the mechanics of 4WD transmissions.

Compulsory military service, with its obvious drawbacks, does at least introduce many of us to the joys of 4WD in the

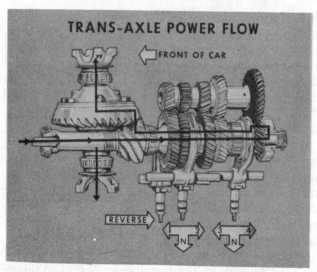

Fig 11.13   FWD transaxle of Ford Taunus saloon.

form of those general purpose vehicles the Jeep and the Land-Rover. In this type of vehicle front wheel drive is only engaged when extra traction is needed for badly surfaced roads or when there is no road. When 4WD is to be used continuously on a hard well-finished road surface as would be the case with a 4WD racing car, it becomes necessary to provide a free-wheel device (i.e. an over-run clutch) in the drive to the front wheels. Apart from possible variations in tyre diameter when one tyre can be more worn than another, the rear wheels always cut corners more than the steered front wheels. With no provision to balance these different drive speeds the transmission shafts would gradually wind up in the manner of a torsion spring. With wide tyres and high-grip compounds it would be inadvisable to expect the rear tyres to slip at a high enough rate to keep the stresses in the drive shafts down to an acceptable level. This is only one of the minor problems that face the designer of a 4WD racing car. Let us see what we can learn from the experiences of one company who have been making 4WD cars since 1950.

The Ferguson 4WD Cars

Ferguson Research Ltd., with the financial backing of Harry Ferguson, the millionaire tractor manufacturer, was founded to develop the four wheel drive and *four wheel steering* ideas that had already involved ex-racing drivers Fred Dixon and Major Tony Rolt in the production of a strange vehicle called 'The Crab'. This vehicle, if it proved nothing else, demonstrated to its designers that four wheel steering is inherently unstable, but with the help of the Ferguson fortune and additional technical assistance from such able designers as Claude Hill their concentrated efforts during the Fifties culminated in an ingenious 4WD vehicle designed primarily to give safe high speed travel under all road conditions.

As shown schematically in Fig 11.14 two pairs of gears plus two one-way clutches make up a control differential called the 'Duolok' control unit. A chain drive is used to take the drive across to the front output shaft and a master differential is used to divide the torque in the chosen percentage split between the front and rear drives. The Duolok control unit permits the shafts driving the front wheels and the rear wheels to revolve at different speeds, but prevents this difference exceeding a prescribed percentage of the average speed. The master differential is an epicyclic gear train to apportion the torque split from the front to rear.

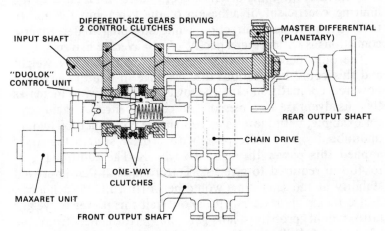

Fig 11.14   Ferguson 4WD transmission (schematic).

This percentage can only be changed by an actual change in the sizes of the sun and planet gears. While all four wheels are gripping the road the central master differential apportions torque between front and rear wheels in the designed ratio. As soon as one wheel spins by more than 10 per cent of its correct speed however, the control system locks up and applies the surplus torque to the opposite end of the car. This Duolock system also operates during braking, a most desirable able safety feature. The control system transfers braking torque through the drive shafts from one end of the car to the other. depending upon which end of the car has a locking wheel. Such a system, though, is not able to cope with the situation where one front wheel and one rear wheel are locking at the same time. This can easily happen when one side of a car runs over a flooded margin during braking. For complete braking control on all wheels the Ferguson Company use the Dunlop Maxaret anti-lock system (described in Chapter Six) which automatically releases brake pressure on any wheel as its speed falls by a designed percentage of its correct road speed. The combination of the Ferguson Duolok control unit and the Dunlop Maxaret system will therefore give completely stable braking under the worst road conditions. It is even possible to use the brakes with safety while taking a bend at speed on a flooded road surface. Stopping distance is of course still related to the limiting coefficient of adhesion of the tyres, but the ability to control the car's direction while stopping under adverse conditions is within the capacity of any average driver.

The only penalty of the Ferguson 4WD system is weight and this could be a serious disadvantage in one of the lower powered competition cars. As power to weight ratio increases this disadvantage becomes of less consequence. A racing car, for example, with more than 1000 horse power per ton, would undoubtedly be handicapped with a drive system that only applied this power through two wheels. The additional 300 to 400 lb required to give a 4WD transmission that improved stability at the same time would be worthwhile in such a car. 3-litre racing sports cars with about half this power to weight ratio would probably not gain in performance from the adoption of 4WD, but they would, without doubt, be much safer cars.

An interesting sports car designed and raced by Peter Westbury of Felday Engineering Ltd. to win the British Hill-Climb Championship in 1963 was the Felday 4, a car that was designed to incorporate the basic Ferguson system as described above. The Felday 4 was quite a *tour de force* for a sports car of this period and was deserving of much greater success than its modest history shows.

The 1880 c.c. BRM V-8 engine, placed behind the driver, transmitted power by one of the shafts inside the propeller shaft tunnel to a six-speed BRM-Ferguson gearbox which was neatly combined with the master differential unit. From the master differential unit (where the torque split occurred) one output shaft passed forwards to drive the front wheels and the other passed backwards to drive the off-set rear bevel box.

The Felday 4 performed extremely well, particularly in the wet and the problems that beset the 1969 Formula 1 4WD cars did not arise, since the Felday 4 was equipped with 13 inch by 8 inch base tyres, a very narrow section by present day standards.

APPENDIX I
The Porsche Type 917

The total output of the Porsche factory at Stuttgart-Zuffen-hausen is about 15 000 cars per annum, a very modest output by any standards, yet the name Porsche is known all over the world for quality and performance. The new development centre at Weissach near Stuttgart is again small by Detroit standards but they have concentrated in this single area a machine shop, a foundry, a body shop, engine test-beds and rolling dynamometers, tyre test drums, test tracks, in fact everything one really needs to develop prototypes of future production cars or 'prototype' sports cars.

Although Porsche withdrew their Works Team from racing in 1971 they continue to assist the Martini Racing Team and the J.W. Gulf Team, who are of course independently sponsored by the makers of the particular liquid products. It is difficult to imagine that Porsche will not return to sports car racing and a successful development in 1972 was a Can-Am turbocharged version of the Type 917 5-litre engine to give at least 800 b.h.p. in long-distance race tune. We are almost certain to see this engine in European racing in the near future.

The 1971 Porsche Type 917 Specification

Weight (empty fuel tanks)	1780 lb
Tank capacity	26.4 Imp. gallons.
Tyres, front	15 in by 9.5 in
Tyres, rear	15 in by 15 in
Drag coefficient, normal body	0.46
Drag coefficient, long tailed body	0.36
Max speed, long tailed body	240 m.p.h.

Engine
Air-cooled flat-12 with Bosch fuel injection, double overhead camshaft valve operation, hemispherical heads with 2 valves per cylinder and two plugs per cylinder.

Capacity	4.998 c.c. (305 cu in)
Bore	86.8 mm (3.42 in)
Stroke	70.4 mm (2.77 in)
Inlet valve diameter	47.5 mm (1.87 in)
Inlet valve lift	12.1 mm (0.477 in)
Exhaust valve diameter	40.5 mm (1.595 in)
Exhaust valve lift	10.5 mm (0.413 in)
Weight (dry)	528 lb
Maximum power	630 b.h.p. at 8300 rev/min
Maximum torque	420 lb ft at 6300 rev/min

THE ENGINE

Porsche have been making a DOHC engine since 1954 when the 550 Spyder first raced with a 1500 c.c. engine. Dr Mezger now claims that the hemispherical head design in the Type 917 will 'induce optimum combustion process' and after 17 years of development work on the same basic head design who would dare to contradict him, unless it be Keith Duckworth who prefers four valves per cylinder and a much small angle between the valves. As seen in Fig A.1 the inlet valve is set at an angle of 30° to the cylinder axis and the exhaust valve at 35°. All valves are sodium cooled, more to improve volumetric efficiency in the case of the inlet valves than to protect them from failure. Valve actuation is by cup tappets as in the majority of the modern DOHC engines.

In the cross-section of the engine shown in Fig A.1 the inlet tract is seen to have a total length from valve head to end of trumpet of about 14.5 inches. From the author's formula for harmonic induction pipe length (see 'The Sports Car'. Chapter Three) one could expect an induction tuning hump at about 6400 rev/min and this is seen to be the case in the power and torque curves for the 5-litre engine which are shown in Fig A.2. The second peak in the power curve which occurs at the maximum power engine speed of 8300 rev/min is almost certainly the result of harmonic exhaust tuning.

The four camshafts are driven by a train of gears as shown in Fig A.3 from a gear situated at the centre of the crankshaft. Herein lies one of the intriguing touches of engineering finesse to be found in this engine, since it solves simultaneously two of the problems associated with long

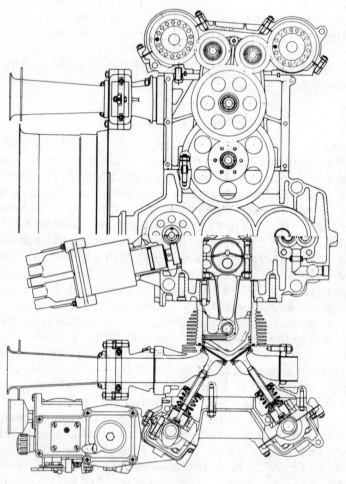

Fig A.1 Porsche 917 two part cross-section.

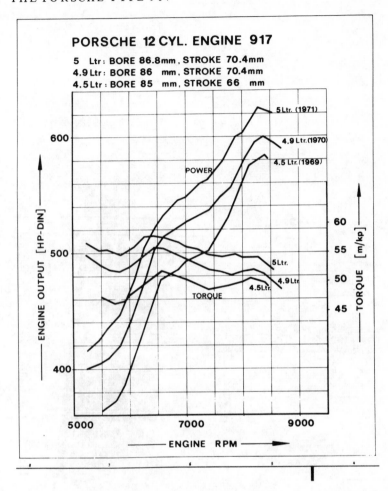

Fig A.2   Power and Torque curves for Porsche 12 Cyl. Engine 917.

crankshafts. The first problem is the danger of excessive
torsional vibrations, the second is the danger of these
vibrations being transferred through the drive trains to the
auxiliaries, in particular to the camshafts which, on long
engines have their own vibration problems. On the Type 917
this central crankshaft pinion drives all the auxiliaries, the
four camshafts, the two ignition distributors and the cooling

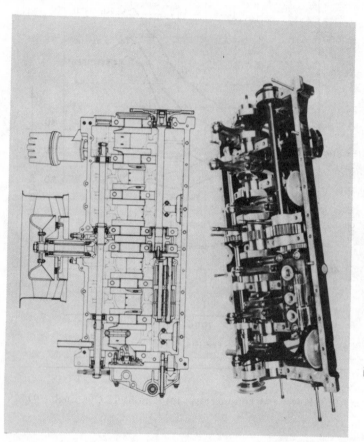

Fig A.3   Longitudinal Section of Racing Engine 917.

236

fan. It also drives the main power take-off shaft through another gearwheel. Torsional vibration in a crankshaft results from the twisting action of each connecting rod acting in turn, according to the firing order, to produce an oscillation relative to the flywheel (or clutch, if the flywheel is minimal). Obviously the crankpin situated at the greatest distance from the flywheel will produce the greatest torsional strain and a long crankshaft will twist through a greater angular deflection than a short one. At the flywheel there is no torsional oscillation. This is called a *node*. Every crankshaft has a *natural* frequency of torsional vibration which depends upon the length and general construction of the shaft. If a crankshaft is to survive for long the *forced* oscillations from the firing frequency must never be allowed to coincide with this natural frequency, since the resulting *resonance* would soon lead to fatigue failure. On some engines this imposes a limit on safe operating speeds. In Fig A.4 it is shown how the 917 crankshaft behaves like two separate shafts with a node situated at the central pinion. This then is not only an ideal place from which to take power out of the system, but is also the one place in the crankshaft where a vibration free drive can be taken to the auxiliaries. The mechanics of it are shown in Fig A.3. The upper view is a vertical cross-section of the engine. The crankcase is in two halves and the lower photograph in Fig A.3 shows an assembled right crankcase-half. The power transmission layshaft is 24 mm (0.945 in) diameter titanium alloy shaft and can be seen in the lower right-hand part of the sectioned view and in the photograph. The crankshaft gear has 32 teeth, the layshaft gear 31. This small difference in the number of teeth is a common engineering precaution to even out tooth wear which could be caused by a feed-back or torsional vibrations in the transmission system. The relatively small diameter layshaft also acts as an excellent shock absorber, taking the place of the propeller shaft which absorbs a surprising amount of 'wind-up' in the conventional transmission layout. The upper layshaft shown in the two views is also driven by the crankshaft pinion and in the upper drawing it can be seen to drive the cooling fan through two bevel gears. This layshaft

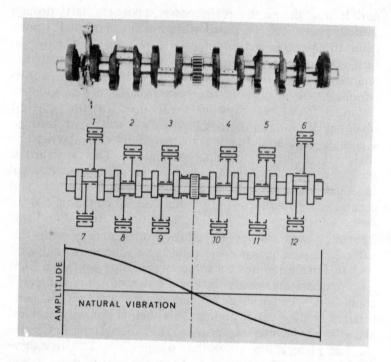

Fig A.4   Crankshaft 917 Racing Engine.

also drives the two ignition distributors and the alternator, but the drive to the three crankcase oil pumps is provided by a pinion from the front end of the output layshaft. The gear train to drive the four camshafts is also taken from this central pinion and the five gears required between this drive pinion and each camshaft can be seen to the right of the engine cross-section of Fig A.1.

Many designers in the past have had a tendency to regard engine lubrication as a simple matter of providing large enough pumps and drilled and cored passages to all the right places. Pressure distribution throughout the entire crankshaft system alone can be so uneven that some bearings receive as much as twice the flow received by others and this in turn means that some cylinders run with a much lower splash feed and that some piston temperatures are also adversely affected. On a typical engine with power take-off from the rear and a timing chain or gears at the front it is customary to feed oil from the pressure pump through drillings in the front and rear main journals. Typical examples are shown in the upper and middle drawings in Fig A.5 which are respectively

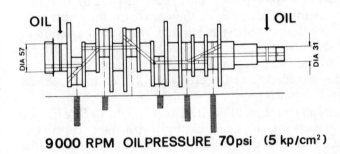

9000 RPM OILPRESSURE 70psi (5 kp/cm²)

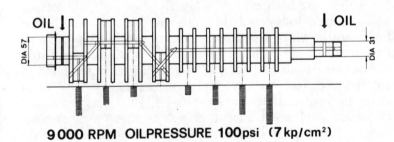

9000 RPM OILPRESSURE 100psi (7 kp/cm²)

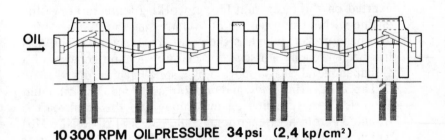

10300 RPM OILPRESSURE 34psi (2,4 kp/cm²)

Fig A.5   Lubrication of Connecting Rod Bearings.

the Type 911 flat-6 crankshaft and the Type 908 flat-8 crankshaft. On the Type 917 with its central power take-off both ends of the crankshaft are free for entry of oil by axial passages. This has not only reduced the pressure drop at entry but has given a much more even distribution along the whole crankshaft. A feed pressure as low as 35 lb/in^2 gave satisfactory bearing lubrication at speeds as high as 10 300 rev/min. The pressure release valve, normally set to 70 lb/in^2 does not return surplus oil to the crankcase since this only adds to the splash problems created by the whirling action of the crankshaft. Instead the overflow from the release valve is returned to the inlet side of the pressure pump. Six scavenge pumps are provided, one for each end of the crankcase and one for each cambox.

Sand-cast magnesium alloy RZ5 (equivalent to S.A.E. spec ZE41A) is used for all engine castings with the exception of the cylinder head which is cast in aluminium alloy with a high strength at working temperature. The cylinder barrels are high-strength aluminium alloy forgings as in all Porsche engines made today and the bores receive a special chrome treatment in which the chrome deposit receives a pattern of tiny dimples to assist in the retention of an oil film for piston lubrication. Heads and barrels are entirely separate units and are mounted on the half-crankcase casting by long studs made in a special steel called Dilavar which has a thermal expansion coefficient almost as high as that for aluminium and magnesium. Since these studs do not reach as high a temperature as the cylinder barrels a higher pressure will be exerted on the head joint face at working temperature of the engine without any danger of overstressing the stud material. The head gasket, which is shown in cross-section in Fig A.1, has been used by Porsche for many years and consists of a C-shaped metal ring supported by a spiral steel spring.

The connecting rods and rod bolts are made of titanium alloy as in most racing engines today and the crankshaft is machined from a case-hardening alloy steel (17Cr 6 Ni 6 Mo) which is tough enough and hard enough for the central gear pinion to be capable of transmitting a maximum torque of 420 lb ft without undue stress or wear.

Fig A.6   Porshe 917 Engine.

The other light material used in the engine is seen in the cooling fan and cooling ducts and in the induction trumpets. These are all moulded in fibre glass reinforced plastic. The high percentage of light alloys and plastics used in this engine have resulted in a total weight of only 528 lb, or 0.84 lb per horse-power. If one includes the weight of the radiators and coolant in any liquid-cooled comparison it would be difficult to find any unsupercharged engine that could challenge the 917 on this basis.

Bosch mechanical fuel injection is used with 12 separate plungers of the type described in Chapter Ten. The pump is driven by an inverted toothed belt from the left-hand inlet-side camshaft (see Fig A.6). A magnesium alloy pump body was specially developed for this engine. Fuel at an injection pressure of 250 lb/in^2 is taken by Nylon tubing to the injectors which are located at the outer ends of the inlet trumpets to give downstream injection.

THE TRANSMISSION

The transaxle casing is made in the sand-cast magnesium alloy RZ5, as used for the main engine castings. A triple disc clutch, using sintered-metal linings is mounted at the front and the drive from this passes via a quill shaft to the rear of the gearbox, as shown in Fig A.7. Porsche-type baulk-ring synchromesh is used on all four forward gears. The fifth gear, for which provision was made in the original design, was not found to be necessary. A limited slip differential is provided in the final drive assembly, the percentage slip at lock-up being adjustable.

THE FRAME AND BODY

Although Porsche were attracted to the use of a monocoque construction they decided against this since it makes subsequent modification so expensive and time consuming. To make their vehicle competitive, however, they adopted the use of aluminium alloy tubing for the frame, since their earlier experience of this material used for the frame of a Type 907 which competed in the Daytona 24 Hours had been entirely satisfactory. As a precaution against failure the interior space of the whole tubular system was interconnected by suitable drillings and filled with compressed air so that periodic checks on this pressure would give warning of incipient cracking. The tubing used is of fairly high tensile strength (52 000 lb/in^2) and all joints were made using argon-arc welding. Since the frame also acts as the supporting structure for the relatively weak body a total weight of only 104 lb for the frame on a 600 horse-power car is quite an

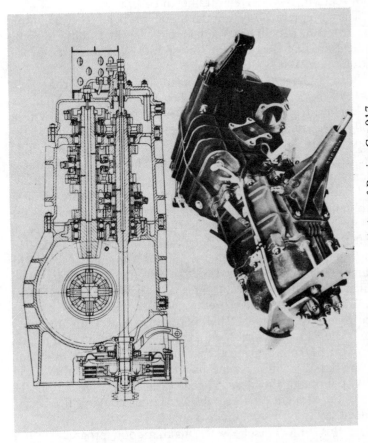

Fig A.7 Transmission of Racing Car 917.

243

achievement. The sheet-steel unitized frame, which included an integral roof and windscreen support structure, on the original GT 40 Ford weighed 300 lb and the 1967 J-car (which became the GT40 Mk IV) and used bonded aluminium honeycomb panels, a modern aircraft technique, still weighed 179 lb, although this structure again included a roof section, a windscreen frame and a firewall.

The complete body on the standard Type 917, including the interior panelling, weighed only 93 lb and there is no indication that any carbon fibre reinforcing was used in the moulding of this body.

Porsche have been aerodynamically minded from their earliest models. They had to be, for with only 40 horsepower available in the Type 356, a good shape of low drag body was needed to give a top speed of 85–90 m.p.h. On the Porsche 904, with a maximum of 155 m.p.h. from 180 b.h.p., the drag coefficient was about 0.36. The conflicting requirements of low-drag and stability at speed have been discussed in Chapter Seven. Porsche were not only well aware of these problems but were also reluctant to give up the search for the ideal shape that would give both low drag and stability at speed. The first *langheck* (long-tailed in English) Type 917 appeared in 1969. Porsche were not too happy with the Kamm-tail concept (see Chapter Seven) since their short-tailed cars, although stable at speed, had a drag coefficient well above 0.40. The 1969 long-tailed bodies gave a drag coefficient of about 0.33, which is very low. With this body the Type 917 was capable of a top speed of about 220 m.p.h. from the 560 b.h.p. given at that time from the 4.5-litre version of the flat-12 engine. At speeds above 200 m.p.h. stability was very poor and the driver needed the whole width of the Mulsanne straight to keep the car under control, if one can indeed say the car was under control.

At this time Porsche were making good progress with a type of aerodynamic levelling device that we venture to suggest should not be completely forgotten, even though the ban on all moveable aerodynamic devices introduced in 1970 by the F.I.A. after several less competent aerofoil experimenters had brought the devices into disrepute forced Porsche to shelve their project. Who can tell when such a

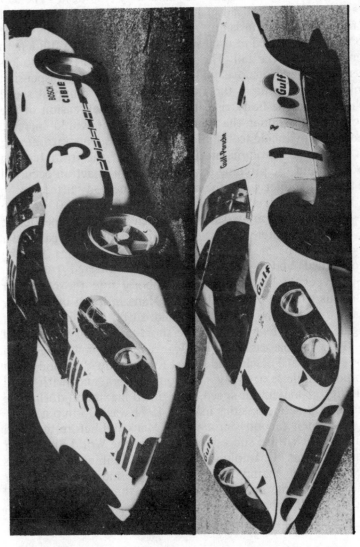

Fig A.8   Sports Racing Car Type 917. Upper: 1971 Le Mans body (long tail). Lower: 1971 Normal body (short tail).

device may not become essential to hold down those 200 m.p.h. commuter trains we shall all be travelling in before the end of the decade? This aerodynamically stabilized Type 917 was actually in the lead at Le Mans for a time in 1969, but it retired with transmission troubles. Two inclined moveable spoilers were fitted at each side at the front with a full length aerofoil above the tail. The incidence angles of these spoilers were arranged to move under the control of the suspension links. If for example the front wheels hit a bump at speed which made the body rise at the front, the extension of the front springs under the rebound movement would increase the angle of incidence of the front spoilers thus introducing an additional aerodynamic downthrust at the front tending to damp out the pitching tendency. A similar action occurred at the rear spoiler when the rear end of the body lifted.

With only fixed aerofoils permitted in 1970 Porsche designed a new long-tailed body which had a drag coefficient of 0.36. Computer calculations indicated that this particular body would be much more likely to win at Le Mans than the short-tailed body. Fortunately Porsche entered cars with both types of body (Fig A.8). Nobody told the computer that this would be the wettest Le Mans in living memory or that some of the Porsches would suffer the indignity of engine failure. Even though the short-tailed body was fitted to the winning car the significance of the new long-tailed body was that Porsche had at last found a low-drag body that would handle extremely well on corners and with good stability at maximum speed. The timed maximum during the Test-Day practice sessions in April 1971 was 235 m.p.h.

After their second victory at Le Mans and before they had clinched their third successive victory in the World Sports Car Manufacturers Championship, Dennis Jenkinson who has seen so many champions come and go said in *Motor Sport* 'the 917 Porsche has turned out to be the car of the decade' and this will probably be seen to be true.

The F.I.A. and the Control of Sports Car Racing

The Establishment in the Realm of Motor Sport is the Federation Internationale de l'Automobile (the F.I.A.) which is an organization made up of representatives from the principal automobile clubs throughout the world. Various committees have special interests in such matters as Touring, Customs and Road Traffic, but the committee responsible for all motor sport (with the exception of Karting) is the Commission Sportive Internationale (the C.S.I.) which is made up of representatives from the National Automobile Clubs or National Associations (the ACNs) and has eighteen members of which six are representative of what are called 'great manufacturing countries'. The current C.S.I. President is Prince P. A. von Metternich.

The Sub-Commission for Safety and Circuits

This sub-committee of the C.S.I. is a very important and much maligned body of responsible men. Any safety matter, whether it be concerned with the design of the vehicle, the protection of the driver, or the protection and enclosure of the public is the concern of this sub-committee. New circuits are inspected by them and safety precautions such as guard rails and safety fences are specified by them. Their activities in recent years have resulted in the installation of automatic fire protection on certain Groups of car, of the introduction of flexible-bag fuel tanks, of oil-catch tanks (to prevent oil spillage from crankcase breathers) and the framing of regulations (not at all popular, this one) to limit the dimensions and mounting positions of aerofoils. This sub-committee have undoubtedly saved a few lives and this must give them some consolation.

The Sub-Committee for Sporting Regulations

This sub-committee also find it difficult to keep all the customers happy. Occasionally they are even accused of

changing the rules just to spike somebody's guns! It is their
awesome responsibility to define and amend from time to
time Appendix 'J' of the International Sporting Code, which
defines the Classification and the Specifications of the cars
taking part in Motor Racing. By Article 251 of this Appendix
the following Categories and Groups are recognized in 1973:-

Category A : recognized production cars (numbers between
brackets being those of the required minimum production in
12 consecutive months).
  Group 1 : series-production touring cars (5 000).
  Group 2 : special touring cars (1 000).
  Group 3 : series-production grand touring cars (1 000).
  Group 4 : special grand touring cars (500).
Category B : experimental competition cars.
  Group 5 : sports cars.
Category C : racing cars.
  Group 7 : two-seater racing cars.
  Group 8 : International formula racing cars.
  Group 9 : 'Formula Libre' racing cars.

GROUPS 3 4 and 5

Under the existing rules our interests in this particular book
are confined to cars under these three Groups, with special
interest in Group 5. Here then is a resumé of the regulations
that apply to these cars. The reader is warned however that
the full text of the rules issued by the F.I.A. should always
be consulted when actual competition is contemplated.

Group 3

These are series-production grand touring cars fitted with at
least two seats, full road equipment and a spare wheel.
Certain small modifications are permitted such as the fitting
of additional head lights, the use of an overdrive, choice of
two final drive ratios, modified dampers (so long as the type
of damper mounting brackets are unchanged) and a change to
racing type brake pads or linings. No engine modifications are
permitted but the engine can be selectively reassembled,
keeping within the maker's dimensional tolerances. This

technique called 'blueprinting' can yield about 2 per cent increase in maximum power on some engines. The bodywork must remain standard, but overriders can be removed and painted-on registration numbers used. Rear wheel spats cannot even be removed if fitted as standard. Examples of Group 3 GT cars are the Lancia Fulvia, the Lotus Europa, and the MGB GT.

Group 4

This Special GT Group must also carry full road equipment and a spare wheel. At one time a production of only 100 cars per annum was sufficient for *homologation* (this being the acceptance for racing in a particular group by the C.S.I.), but today the increase to a minimum of 500 has forced many specialist sports car manufacturers out of this group.

Group 4 cars can have their engines modified to produce more power. Machine operations are permitted on all standard (stock) engine components, such as the cylinder head, block and crankcase. Components can be changed in shape, lightened, dynamically balanced, etc., but cannot be replaced by other castings of a lighter or stronger material. No special surface treatments, such as metal spraying are permitted. All this of course gives complete freedom to the fitting of larger valves and the opening out of ports, but the number of valves per cylinder cannot be changed. If a tuner can see his way to fit two plugs per cylinder by additional machining, but not by the omission of any of the original maker's machining, he is free to do this.

The induction system can be modified in any manner desired, with two exceptions: *direct* fuel injection which means directly into the combustion chambers and not into the ports) can only be used if in the maker's specification; supercharging (with the appropriate multiplication factor of 1.4 applied to the cubic capacity) can only be used if the car is supercharged in standard form by the maker. Any type of exhaust system is permitted during the race. For events on open roads, however, it must meet the noise suppression requirements of the particular country. The oil sump may be modified or replaced by one of larger capacity. External oil coolers must be below wheel-hub height and cannot extend beyond the normal body perimeter or involve any additional 'aerodynamic' ducting. A larger or improved oil pump may be fitted, but the number of pumps cannot be increased.

While larger valves and ports, modified port shapes and different camshafts and valve springs may be fitted, it is not permitted to increase the number of valves per cylinder or the number, location or driving system of the maker's camshaft(s). Any conceivable change or modification to the piston, gudgeon pin (wrist pin) or piston rings is permitted.

The gear ratios can be changed but not the number of gears. A limited-slip differential may be incorporated so long as the manufacturer's standard axle can be modified to take it. Any type of F.I.A. - approved wheel is permitted in Group 4 so long as all four wheels are of the same size and the tyres do not extend beyond that part of the bodywork that acts as a mudguard and that this 'mudguard' wraps around at least one-third of the tyre circumference. Wing extensions are permitted to a maximum increase of 5 cm (1.97 inches) per side, so the use of wider tyres and rims is permitted within these extra limits.

Options

To complicate still further a set of rules that are already very complicated it is permissible in this Group to avail oneself of a whole list of options, provided the makers have supplied at least 100 units in the year. This permits the manufacturers to develop special racing components, more robust crankshafts, connecting rods, transmission components and improved suspension parts. A full list of possible options is given in Appendix 'J'.

Group 5

This is the only group that still carries the name 'sports car' under the current Appendix 'J' classification. Only one vehicle need actually be made to race in this group but to compete seriously in this group most manufacturers would make at least ten in order to keep a team in the field. Besides the cars specially made to race in this group cars that have been too extensively modified to comply with the rules of Group 4 can also compete. They must, of course, not infringe the few basic rules laid down for Group 5 which are, briefly, as follows:

Bodywork may be completely enclosed or completely open, but a small bubble-canopy (as in speed record type vehicles) over the driver's head with a hole or a detachable cover where the passenger could be seated is not permitted. The minimum internal dimensions of the body and seating are closely defined under Appendix 'J'. Open cars need not carry a windscreen but the opening in the upper surface for the driver and passenger must be placed symmetrically relative to the longitudinal centre-line of the car. The body must enclose the wheels in plan (as specified for Group 4) and must extend downwards at the rear for the full width of the tyres to within 20 cm (7.8 inches) minimum distance from the ground. It is not necessary to carry a spare wheel and no luggage compartment is necessary.

Aerofoils, or 'aerodynamic devices' are permitted and are defined in a manner that effectively precludes the use of aerofoils mounted on tall masts at a considerable height above the body. The rules state that the highest point of any forward facing gap in the coachwork shall not be situated above a horizontal plane which is 80 cm (31.5 inches) above the lowest point of the entirely sprung structure of the car. Since the coachwork cannot exceed the width of the wheels by a total of 20 cm (7.8 inches) this also places a maximum width on any front or rear spoilers or aerofoils.

Minimum Weights
Sports cars must comply with the following minimum weights:

Engine capacity below or equal to 500 c.c.	450 kg
Engine capacity from 500 to 600 c.c.	460 kg
Engine capacity from 600 to 700 c.c.	470 kg
Engine capacity from 700 to 850 c.c.	480 kg
Engine capacity from 850 to 1000 c.c.	500 kg
Engine capacity from 1000 to 1150 c.c.	510 kg
Engine capacity from 1150 to 1300 c.c.	525 kg
Engine capacity from 1300 to 1600 c.c.	550 kg
Engine capacity from 1600 to 2000 c.c.	575 kg

Engine capacity from 2000 to 2500 c.c.   600 kg
Engine capacity from 2500 to 3000 c.c.   650 kg
Engine capacity from 3000 to 4000 c.c.   700 kg
Engine capacity from 4000 to 5000 c.c.   750 kg
Engine capacity from 5000 to 6000 c.c.   775 kg
Engine capacity over 6000 cc   800 kg

Sports Car Championship

The World Championship for Makes in 1972 is confined to Group 5 sports cars up to 3-litres in engine capacity or to Group 4 special grand touring cars of unlimited capacity.

Events

Qualifying events must be at least 1000 km in length or of at least 6 hours duration. The following are the qualifying events for 1973:

1000 km of Buenos Aires	Targa Florio
24 hours of Daytona	1000 km of Nürburgring
6 hours of Vellelunga	24 hours of Le Mans
Dijon	1000 km of Österreichring
1000 of Monza	6 hours of Watkins Glen
1000 km of Spa.	

Index